Glencoe Mathematics

Algebra 1

Chapter 5
Resource Masters

McGraw Hill Glencoe

New York, New York   Columbus, Ohio   Chicago, Illinois   Peoria, Illinois   Woodland Hills, California

CONSUMABLE WORKBOOKS Many of the worksheets contained in the Chapter Resource Masters booklets are available as consumable workbooks in both English and Spanish.

	ISBN10	ISBN13
Study Guide and Intervention Workbook	0-07-877228-1	978-0-07-877228-3
Skills Practice Workbook	0-07-877230-3	978-0-07-877230-6
Practice Workbook	0-07-877232-X	978-0-07-877232-0
Word Problem Practice Workbook	0-07-877234-6	978-0-07-877234-4

Spanish Versions

	ISBN10	ISBN13
Study Guide and Intervention Workbook	0-07-877229-X	978-0-07-877229-0
Skills Practice Workbook	0-07-877231-1	978-0-07-877231-3
Practice Workbook	0-07-877233-8	978-0-07-877233-7
Word Problem Practice Workbook	0-07-877235-4	978-0-07-877235-1

ANSWERS FOR WORKBOOKS The answers for Chapter 5 of these workbooks can be found in the back of this Chapter Resource Masters booklet.

StudentWorks Plus™ This CD-ROM includes the entire Student Edition text along with the English workbooks listed above.

TeacherWorks Plus™ All of the materials found in this booklet are included for viewing, printing, and editing in this CD-ROM.

Spanish Assessment Masters (ISBN10: 0-07-877236-2, ISBN13: 978-0-07-877236-8) These masters contain a Spanish version of Chapter 5 Test Form 2A and Form 2C.

Send all inquiries to:
The McGraw-Hill Companies
8787 Orion Place
Columbus, OH 43240

ISBN13: 978-0-07-873948-4
ISBN10: 0-07-873948-9

Algebra 1 CRM5

Printed in the United States of America

2 3 4 5 6 7 8 9 10 024 13 12 11 10 09 08 07

Contents

Teacher's Guide to Using the
Chapter 5 Resource Masters

The *Chapter 5 Resource Masters* includes the core materials needed for Chapter 5. These materials include worksheets, extensions, and assessment options. The answers for these pages appear at the back of this booklet.

All of the materials found in this booklet are included for viewing and printing on the *TeacherWorks Plus™* CD-ROM.

Chapter Resources

Student-Built Glossary (pages 1-2) These masters are a student study tool that presents up to twenty of the key vocabulary terms from the chapter. Students are to record definitions and/or examples for each term. You may suggest that students highlight or star the terms with which they are not familiar. Give this to students before beginning Lesson 5-1. Encourage them to add these pages to their mathematics study notebooks. Remind them to complete the appropriate words as they study each lesson.

Anticipation Guide (pages 3-4) This master, presented in both English and Spanish, is a survey used before beginning the chapter to pinpoint what students may or may not know about the concepts in the chapter. Students will revisit this survey after they complete the chapter to see if their perceptions have changed.

Lesson Resources

Lesson Reading Guide Get Ready for the Lesson extends the discussion from the beginning of the Student Edition lesson. Read the Lesson asks students to interpret the context of and relationships among terms in the lesson. Finally, Remember What You Learned asks students to summarize what they have learned using various representation techniques. Use as a study tool for note taking or as an informal reading assignment. It is also a helpful tool for ELL (English Language Learners).

Study Guide and Intervention These masters provide vocabulary, key concepts, additional worked-out examples and Check Your Progress exercises to use as a reteaching activity. It can also be used in conjunction with the Student Edition as an instructional tool for students who have been absent.

Skills Practice This master focuses more on the computational nature of the lesson. Use as an additional practice option or as homework for second-day teaching of the lesson.

Practice This master closely follows the types of problems found in the Exercises section of the Student Edition and includes word problems. Use as an additional practice option or as homework for second-day teaching of the lesson.

Word Problem Practice This master includes additional practice in solving word problems that apply the concepts of the lesson. Use as an additional practice or as homework for second-day teaching of the lesson.

Enrichment These activities may extend the concepts of the lesson, offer an historical or multicultural look at the concepts, or widen students' perspectives on the mathematics they are learning. They are written for use with all levels of students.

Graphing Calculator, Scientific Calculator, or Spreadsheet Activities These activities present ways in which technology can be used with the concepts in some lessons of this chapter. Use as an alternative approach to some concepts or as an integral part of your lesson presentation.

Assessment Options

The assessment masters in the *Chapter 5 Resource Masters* offer a wide range of assessment tools for formative (monitoring) assessment and summative (final) assessment.

Student Recording Sheet This master corresponds with the standardized test practice at the end of the chapter.

Pre-AP Rubric This master provides information for teachers and students on how to assess performance on open-ended questions.

Quizzes Four free-response quizzes offer assessment at appropriate intervals in the chapter.

Mid-Chapter Test This 1-page test provides an option to assess the first half of the chapter. It parallels the timing of the Mid-Chapter Quiz in the Student Edition and includes both multiple-choice and free-response questions.

Vocabulary Test This test is suitable for all students. It includes a list of vocabulary words and 10 questions to assess students' knowledge of those words. This can also be used in conjunction with one of the leveled chapter tests.

Leveled Chapter Tests

- *Form 1* contains multiple-choice questions and is intended for use with below grade level students.
- *Forms 2A and 2B* contain multiple-choice questions aimed at on grade level students. These tests are similar in format to offer comparable testing situations.
- *Forms 2C and 2D* contain free-response questions aimed at on grade level students. These tests are similar in format to offer comparable testing situations.
- *Form 3* is a free-response test for use with above grade level students.

All of the above mentioned tests include a free-response Bonus question.

Extended-Response Test Performance assessment tasks are suitable for all students. Sample answers and a scoring rubric are included for evaluation.

Standardized Test Practice These three pages are cumulative in nature. It includes three parts: multiple-choice questions with bubble-in answer format, griddable questions with answer grids, and short-answer free-response questions.

Answers

- The answers for the Anticipation Guide and Lesson Resources are provided as reduced pages with answers appearing in red.
- Full-size answer keys are provided for the assessment masters.

5   Student-Built Glossary

This is an alphabetical list of the key vocabulary terms you will learn in Chapter 5. As you study the chapter, complete each term's definition or description. Remember to add the page number where you found the term. Add these pages to your Algebra Study Notebook to review vocabulary at the end of the chapter.

Vocabulary Term	Found on Page	Definition/Description/Example
consistent kuhn·SIHS·tuhnt		
dependent		
elimination ih·LIH·muh·NAY·shuhn		
independent		
inconsistent		

(continued on the next page)

5 Student-Built Glossary *(continued)*

Vocabulary Term	Found on Page	Definition/Description/Example
substitution SUHB·stuh·TOO·shuhn		
system of equations		

5 Anticipation Guide

Solving Systems of Linear Equations

Step 1 *Before you begin Chapter 5*

- Read each statement.
- Decide whether you Agree (A) or Disagree (D) with the statement.
- Write A or D in the first column OR if you are not sure whether you agree or disagree, write NS (Not Sure).

STEP 1 A, D, or NS	Statement	STEP 2 A or D
	1. A solution of a system of equations is any ordered pair that satisfies one of the equations	
	2. A system of equations of parallel lines will have no solutions.	
	3. A system of equations of two perpendicular lines will have infinitely many solutions.	
	4. It is not possible to have exactly two solutions to a system of linear equations.	
	5. The most accurate way to solve a system of equations is to graph the equations to see where they intersect.	
	6. To solve a system of equations, such as $2x - y = 21$ and $3y = 2x - 6$, by substitution, solve one of the equations for one variable and substitute the result into the other equation.	
	7. When solving a system of equations, a result that is a true statement, such as $-5 = -5$, means the equations do not share a common solution.	
	8. Mutually exclusive events are events that cannot happen Adding the equations $3x - 4y = 8$ and $2x + 4y = 7$ results in a 0 coefficient for y.	
	9. The equation $7x - 2y = 12$ can be multiplied by 2 so that the coefficient of y is -4.	
	10. The result of multiplying $-7x - 3y = 11$ by -3 is $-1x + 9y = 11$.	

Step 2 *After you complete Chapter 5*

- Reread each statement and complete the last column by entering an A or a D.
- Did any of your opinions about the statements change from the first column?
- For those statements that you mark with a D, use a piece of paper to write an example of why you disagree.

5 Ejercicios preparatorios

Resuelve sistemas de ecuaciones lineales

Antes de comenzar el Capítulo 5

- Lee cada enunciado.

- Decide si estás de acuerdo (A) o en desacuerdo (D) con el enunciado.

- Escribe A o D en la primera columna O si no estás seguro(a) de la respuesta, escribe NS (No estoy seguro(a).

PASO 1 A, D o NS	Enunciado	PASO 2 A o D
	1. Una solución de un sistema de ecuaciones es cualquier par ordenado que satisface una de las ecuaciones	
	2. Un sistema de ecuaciones de rectas paralelas no tendrá soluciones.	
	3. Un sistema de ecuaciones de dos rectas perpendiculares tendrá un número infinito de soluciones.	
	4. No es posible tener exactamente dos soluciones para un sistema de ecuaciones lineales.	
	5. La forma más precisa de resolver un sistema de ecuaciones es graficar las ecuaciones y ver dónde se intersecan.	
	6. Para resolver un sistema de ecuaciones, como $2x - y = 21$ y $3y = 2x - 6$, por sustitución, despeja una variable en una de la ecuaciones y reemplaza el resultado en la otra ecuación.	
	7. Cuando se resuelve un sistema de ecuaciones, un resultado que es un enunciado verdadero, como $-5 = -5$, significa que las ecuaciones no comparten una solución.	
	8. Los eventos mutuamente exclusivos son eventos que no pueden suceder al mismo tiempo. El sumar las ecuaciones $3x - 4y = 8$ y $2x + 4y = 7$ resulta en un coeficiente de 0 para y.	
	9. La ecuación $7x - 2y = 12$ se puede multiplicar por 2, de modo que el coeficiente de y es -4.	
	10. El resultado de multiplicar $-7x - 3y = 11$ por -3 es $-1x + 9y = 11$.	

Después de completar el Capítulo 5

- Vuelve a leer cada enunciado y completa la última columna con una A o una D.

- ¿Cambió cualquiera de tus opiniones sobre los enunciados de la primera columna?

- En una hoja de papel aparte, escribe un ejemplo de por qué estás en desacuerdo con los enunciados que marcaste con una D.

5-1 Lesson Reading Guide

Graphing Systems of Equations

Get Ready for the Lesson

Read the introduction to Lesson 7-1 in your textbook.

• What is meant by the term *linear function*?

• What does it mean to say that *two lines intersect*?

Read the Lesson

1. Each figure shows the graph of a system of two equations. Write the letter of the figures that illustrate each statement.

A.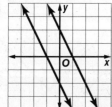

B.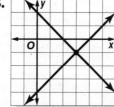

C.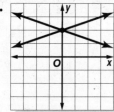

D.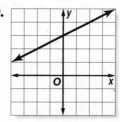

    a. A system of two linear equations can have an infinite number of solutions.

    b. A system of equations is consistent if there is at least one ordered pair that satisfies both equations.

    c. If two graphs are parallel, there are no ordered pairs that satisfy both equations.

    d. If a system of equations has exactly one solution, it is independent.

    e. If a system of equations has an infinite number of solutions, it is dependent.

Remember What You Learned

2. Describe how you can solve a system of equations by graphing.

5-1 Study Guide and Intervention

Graphing Systems of Equations

Number of Solutions Two or more linear equations involving the same variables form a **system of equations**. A solution of the system of equations is an ordered pair of numbers that satisfies both equations. The table below summarizes information about systems of linear equations.

Graph of a System	intersecting lines	same line	parallel lines
Number of Solutions	exactly one solution	infinitely many solutions	no solution
Terminology	consistent and independent	consistent and dependent	inconsistent

Example Use the graph at the right to determine whether the system has *no* solution, *one* solution, or *infinitely many* solutions.

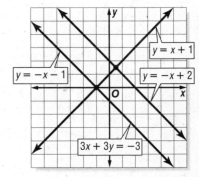

a. $y = -x + 2$
$y = x + 1$

Since the graphs of $y = -x + 2$ and $y = x + 1$ intersect, there is one solution.

b. $y = -x + 2$
$3x + 3y = -3$

Since the graphs of $y = -x + 2$ and $3x + 3y = -3$ are parallel, there are no solutions.

c. $3x + 3y = -3$
$y = -x - 1$

Since the graphs of $3x + 3y = -3$ and $y = -x - 1$ coincide, there are infinitely many solutions.

Exercises

Use the graph at the right to determine whether each system has *no* solution, *one* solution, or *infinitely many* solutions.

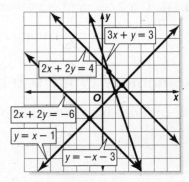

1. $y = -x - 3$
$y = x - 1$

2. $2x + 2y = -6$
$y = -x - 3$

3. $y = -x - 3$
$2x + 2y = 4$

4. $2x + 2y = -6$
$3x + y = 3$

5-1 Study Guide and Intervention (continued)

Graphing Systems of Equations

Solve by Graphing One method of solving a system of equations is to graph the equations on the same coordinate plane.

Example Graph each system of equations. Then determine whether the system has *no* solution, *one* solution, or *infinitely many* solutions. If the system has one solution, name it.

a. $x + y = 2$
$x - y = 4$

The graphs intersect. Therefore, there is one solution. The point $(3, -1)$ seems to lie on both lines. Check this estimate by replacing x with 3 and y with -1 in each equation.

$x + y = 2$
$3 + (-1) = 2$ ✓
$x - y = 4$
$3 - (-1) = 3 + 1$ or 4 ✓

The solution is $(3, -1)$.

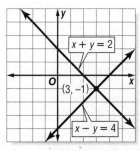

b. $y = 2x + 1$
$2y = 4x + 2$

The graphs coincide. Therefore there are infinitely many solutions.

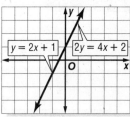

Exercises

Graph each system of equations. Then determine whether the system has *no* solution, *one* solution, or *infinitely many* solutions. If the system has one solution, name it.

1. $y = -2$
$3x - y = -1$

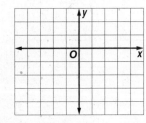

2. $x = 2$
$2x + y = 1$

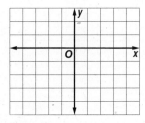

3. $y = \frac{1}{2}x$
$x + y = 3$

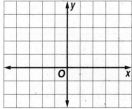

4. $2x + y = 6$
$2x - y = -2$

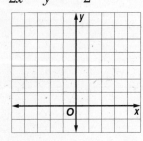

5. $3x + 2y = 6$
$3x + 2y = -4$

6. $2y = -4x + 4$
$y = -2x + 2$

5-1 Skills Practice

Graphing Systems of Equations

Use the graph at the right to determine whether each system has *no* solution, *one* solution, or *infinitely many* solutions.

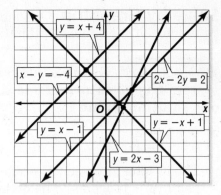

1. $y = x - 1$
  $y = -x + 1$

2. $x - y = -4$
  $y = x + 4$

3. $y = x + 4$
  $2x - 2y = 2$

4. $y = 2x - 3$
  $2x - 2y = 2$

Graph each system of equations. Then determine whether the system has *no* solution, *one* solution, or *infinitely many* solutions. If the system has one solution, name it.

5. $2x - y = 1$
  $y = -3$

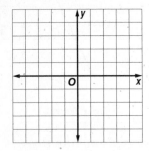

6. $x = 1$
  $2x + y = 4$

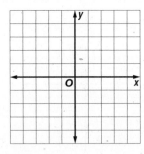

7. $3x + y = -3$
  $3x + y = 3$

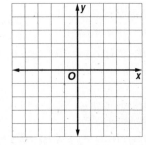

8. $y = x + 2$
  $x - y = -2$

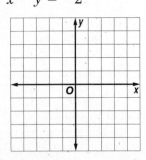

9. $x + 3y = -3$
  $x - 3y = -3$

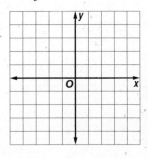

10. $y - x = -1$
  $x + y = 3$

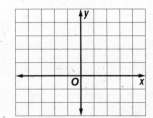

11. $x - y = 3$
  $x - 2y = 3$

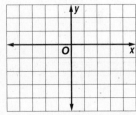

12. $x + 2y = 4$
  $y = -\frac{1}{2}x + 2$

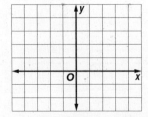

13. $y = 2x + 3$
  $3y = 6x - 6$

5-1 Practice

Graphing Systems of Equations

Use the graph at the right to determine whether each system has *no* solution, *one* solution, or *infinitely many* solutions.

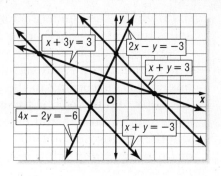

1. $x + y = 3$
$x + y = -3$

2. $2x - y = -3$
$4x - 2y = -6$

3. $x + 3y = 3$
$x + y = -3$

4. $x + 3y = 3$
$2x - y = -3$

Graph each system of equations. Then determine whether the system has *no* solution, *one* solution, or *infinitely many* solutions. If the system has one solution, name it.

5. $3x - y = -2$
$3x - y = 0$

6. $y = 2x - 3$
$4x = 2y + 6$

7. $x + 2y = 3$
$3x - y = -5$

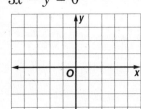

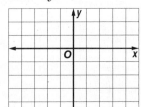

BUSINESS For Exercises 8 and 9, use the following information.

Nick plans to start a home-based business producing and selling gourmet dog treats. He figures it will cost $20 in operating costs per week plus $0.50 to produce each treat. He plans to sell each treat for $1.50.

8. Graph the system of equations $y = 0.5x + 20$ and $y = 1.5x$ to represent the situation.

9. How many treats does Nick need to sell per week to break even?

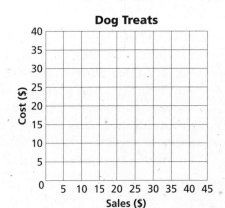

SALES For Exercises 10–12, use the following information.

A used book store also started selling used CDs and videos. In the first week, the store sold 40 used CDs and videos, at $4.00 per CD and $6.00 per video. The sales for both CDs and videos totaled $180.00

10. Write a system of equations to represent the situation.

11. Graph the system of equations.

12. How many CDs and videos did the store sell in the first week?

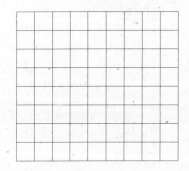

5-1 Word Problem Practice

Graphing Systems of Equations

1. BUSINESS The widget factory will sell a total of y widgets after x days according to the equation $y = 200x + 300$. The gadget factory will sell y gadgets after x days according to the equation $y = 200x + 100$. Look at the graph of the system of equations and determine whether it has *no* solution, *one* solution, or *infinitely many* solutions.

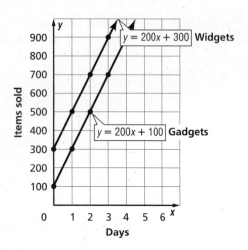

2. ARCHITECTURE An office building has two elevators. One elevator starts out on the 4th floor, 35 feet above the ground, and is descending at a rate of 2.2 feet per second. The other elevator starts out at ground level and is rising at a rate of 1.7 feet per second. Write a system of equations to represent the situation.

3. FITNESS Olivia and her brother William had a bicycle race. Olivia rode at a speed of 20 feet per second while William rode at a speed of 15 feet per second. To be fair, Olivia decided to give William a 150-foot head start. The race ended in a tie. How far away was the finish line from where Olivia started?

AVIATION For Exercises 4 and 5, use the following information.

Two planes are in flight near a local airport. One plane is at an altitude of 1000 meters and is ascending at a rate of 400 meters per minute. The second plane is at an altitude of 5900 meters and is descending at a rate of 300 meters per minute.

4. Write a system of equations that represents the progress of each plane

5. Make a graph that represents the progress of each plane.

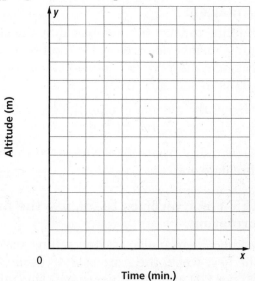

5-1 Enrichment

Graphing a Trip

The distance formula, $d = rt$, is used to solve many types of problems. If you graph an equation such as $d = 50t$, the graph is a model for a car going at 50 mi/h. The time the car travels is t; the distance in miles the car covers is d. The slope of the line is the speed.

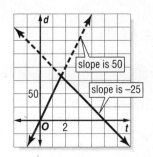

Suppose you drive to a nearby town and return. You average 50 mi/h on the trip out but only 25 mi/h on the trip home. The round trip takes 5 hours. How far away is the town?

The graph at the right represents your trip. Notice that the return trip is shown with a negative slope because you are driving in the opposite direction.

Solve each problem.

1. Estimate the answer to the problem in the above example. About how far away is the town?

2. Graph this trip and solve the problem. An airplane has enough fuel for 3 hours of safe flying. On the trip out the pilot averages 200 mi/h flying against a headwind. On the trip back, the pilot averages 250 mi/h. How long a trip out can the pilot make?

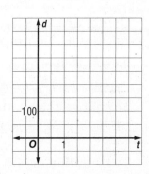

3. Graph this trip and solve the problem. You drive to a town 100 miles away. On the trip out you average 25 mi/h. On the trip back you average 50 mi/h. How many hours do you spend driving?

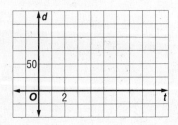

4. Graph this trip and solve the problem. You drive at an average speed of 50 mi/h to a discount shopping plaza, spend 2 hours shopping, and then return at an average speed of 25 mi/h. The entire trip takes 8 hours. How far away is the shopping plaza?

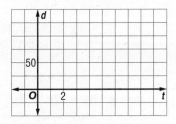

Lesson 5-1

5-1 Graphing Calculator Activity

Solution to a System of Linear Equations

A graphing calculator can be used to solve a system of linear equations graphically. The solution of a system of linear equations can be found by using the **TRACE** feature or by using the **intersect** command under the **CALC** menu.

Example Solve each system of linear equations.

a. $x + y = 0$
  $x - y = -4$

Using TRACE: Solve each equation for y and enter each equation into **Y=**. Then graph using **Zoom 8: ZInteger**. Use **TRACE** to find the solution.

Keystrokes: Y= (−) X,T,θ,n ENTER X,T,θ,n + 4 ZOOM 6
ZOOM 8 ENTER TRACE ◄ ◄ .

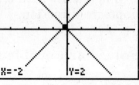
[−47, 47] scl:10 by [−31, 31] scl:10

The solution is $(-2, 2)$.

b. $2x + y = 4$
  $4x + 3y = 3$

Using CALC: Solve each equation for y, enter each into the calculator, and graph. Use **CALC** to determine the solution.

Keystrokes: Y= (−) 2 X,T,θ,n + 4 ENTER ((−) 4 ÷ 3)
X,T,θ,n + 1 ZOOM 6 2nd [CALC] 5 ENTER ENTER ENTER .

To change the x-value to a fraction, press 2nd [QUIT] X,T,θ,n
MATH ENTER ENTER .

[−10, 10] scl:1 by [−10, 10] scl:1

The solution is $(4.5, -5)$ or $\left(\frac{9}{2}, -5\right)$.

Exercises

Solve each system of linear equations.

1. $y = 2$
  $5x + 4y = 18$

2. $y = -x + 3$
  $y = x + 1$

3. $x + y = -1$
  $2x - y = -8$

4. $-3x + y = 10$
  $-x + 2y = 0$

5. $-4x + 3y = 10$
  $7x + y = 20$

6. $5x + 3y = 11$
  $x - 5y = 5$

7. $3x - 2y = -4$
  $-4x + 3y = 5$

8. $3x + 2y = 4$
  $-6x - 4y = -8$

9. $4x - 5y = 0$
  $6x - 5y = 10$

5-2 Lesson Reading Guide

Substitution

Get Ready for the Lesson

Read the introduction to Lesson 5-2 in your textbook.

- What is the system of equations?

- Based on the graph, are there 0, 1, or infinitely many solutions of the system?

Read the Lesson

1. Describe how you would use substitution to solve each system of equations.

   a. $y = -2x$
   $x + 3y = 15$

   b. $3x - 2y = 12$
   $x = 2y$

   c. $x + 2y = 7$
   $2x - 8y = 8$

   d. $-3x + 5y = 81$
   $2x + y = 24$

2. Jess solved a system of equations and her result was $-8 = -8$. All of her work was correct. Describe the graph of the system. Explain.

3. Miguel solved a system of equations and his result was $5 = -2$. All of his work was correct. Describe the graph of the system. Explain.

Remember What You Learned

4. What is usually the first step in solving a system of equations by substitution?

Lesson 5-2

5-2 Study Guide and Intervention

Substitution

Substitution One method of solving systems of equations is **substitution**.

Example 1 Use substitution to solve the system of equations.
$$y = 2x$$
$$4x - y = -4$$

Substitute $2x$ for y in the second equation.

$4x - y = -4$	Second equation
$4x - 2x = -4$	$y = 2x$
$2x = -4$	Combine like terms.
$x = -2$	Divide each side by 2 and simplify.

Use $y = 2x$ to find the value of y.

$y = 2x$	First equation
$y = 2(-2)$	$x = -2$
$y = -4$	Simplify.

The solution is $(-2, -4)$.

Example 2 Solve for one variable, then substitute.
$$x + 3y = 7$$
$$2x - 4y = -6$$

Solve the first equation for x since the coefficient of x is 1.

$x + 3y = 7$	First equation
$x + 3y - 3y = 7 - 3y$	Subtract $3y$ from each side.
$x = 7 - 3y$	Simplify.

Find the value of y by substituting $7 - 3y$ for x in the second equation.

$2x - 4y = -6$	Second equation
$2(7 - 3y) - 4y = -6$	$x = 7 - 3y$
$14 - 6y - 4y = -6$	Distributive Property
$14 - 10y = -6$	Combine like terms.
$14 - 10y - 14 = -6 - 14$	Subtract 14 from each side.
$-10y = -20$	Simplify.
$y = 2$	Divide each side by -10 and simplify.

Use $y = 2$ to find the value of x.
$$x = 7 - 3y$$
$$x = 7 - 3(2)$$
$$x = 1$$
The solution is $(1, 2)$.

Exercises

Use substitution to solve each system of equations. If the system does *not* have exactly one solution, state whether it has *no* solution or *infinitely many* solutions.

1. $y = 4x$
   $3x - y = 1$

2. $x = 2y$
   $y = x - 2$

3. $x = 2y - 3$
   $x = 2y + 4$

4. $x - 2y = -1$
   $3y = x + 4$

5. $c - 4d = 1$
   $2c - 8d = 2$

6. $x + 2y = 0$
   $3x + 4y = 4$

7. $2b = 6a - 14$
   $3a - b = 7$

8. $x + y = 16$
   $2y = -2x + 2$

9. $y = -x + 3$
   $2y + 2x = 4$

10. $x = 2y$
   $0.25x + 0.5y = 10$

11. $x - 2y = -5$
   $x + 2y = -1$

12. $-0.2x + y = 0.5$
   $0.4x + y = 1.1$

5-2 Study Guide and Intervention (continued)

Substitution

Real-World Problems Substitution can also be used to solve real-world problems involving systems of equations. It may be helpful to use tables, charts, diagrams, or graphs to help you organize data.

Example CHEMISTRY How much of a 10% saline solution should be mixed with a 20% saline solution to obtain 1000 milliliters of a 12% saline solution?

Let s = the number of milliliters of 10% saline solution.
Let t = the number of milliliters of 20% saline solution.

Use a table to organize the information.

	10% saline	20% saline	12% saline
Total milliliters	s	t	1000
Milliliters of saline	0.10s	0.20t	0.12(1000)

Write a system of equations.
$s + t = 1000$
$0.10s + 0.20t = 0.12(1000)$
Use substitution to solve this system.

$s + t = 1000$	First equation
$s = 1000 - t$	Solve for s.
$0.10s + 0.20t = 0.12(1000)$	Second equation
$0.10(1000 - t) + 0.20t = 0.12(1000)$	$s = 1000 - t$
$100 - 0.10t + 0.20t = 0.12(1000)$	Distributive Property
$100 + 0.10t = 0.12(1000)$	Combine like terms.
$0.10t = 20$	Simplify.
$\dfrac{0.10t}{0.10} = \dfrac{20}{0.10}$	Divide each side by 0.10.
$t = 200$	Simplify.
$s + t = 1000$	First equation
$s + 200 = 1000$	$t = 200$
$s = 800$	Solve for s.

800 milliliters of 10% solution and 200 milliliters of 20% solution should be used.

Lesson 5-2

Exercises

1. **SPORTS** At the end of the 2000-2001 football season, 31 Super Bowl games had been played with the current two football leagues, the American Football Conference (AFC) and the National Football Conference (NFC). The NFC won five more games than the AFC. How many games did each conference win? **Source:** New York Times Almanac

2. **CHEMISTRY** A lab needs to make 100 gallons of an 18% acid solution by mixing a 12% acid solution with a 20% solution. How many gallons of each solution are needed?

3. **GEOMETRY** The perimeter of a triangle is 24 inches. The longest side is 4 inches longer than the shortest side, and the shortest side is three-fourths the length of the middle side. Find the length of each side of the triangle.

5-2 Skills Practice

Substitution

Use substitution to solve each system of equations. If the system does *not* have exactly one solution, state whether it has *no* solution or *infinitely many* solutions.

1. $y = 4x$
$\quad x + y = 5$

2. $y = 2x$
$\quad x + 3y = -14$

3. $y = 3x$
$\quad 2x + y = 15$

4. $x = -4y$
$\quad 3x + 2y = 20$

5. $y = x - 1$
$\quad x + y = 3$

6. $x = y - 7$
$\quad x + 8y = 2$

7. $y = 4x - 1$
$\quad y = 2x - 5$

8. $y = 3x + 8$
$\quad 5x + 2y = 5$

9. $2x - 3y = 21$
$\quad y = 3 - x$

10. $y = 5x - 8$
$\quad 4x + 3y = 33$

11. $x + 2y = 13$
$\quad 3x - 5y = 6$

12. $x + 5y = 4$
$\quad 3x + 15y = -1$

13. $3x - y = 4$
$\quad 2x - 3y = -9$

14. $x + 4y = 8$
$\quad 2x - 5y = 29$

15. $x - 5y = 10$
$\quad 2x - 10y = 20$

16. $5x - 2y = 14$
$\quad 2x - y = 5$

17. $2x + 5y = 38$
$\quad x - 3y = -3$

18. $x - 4y = 27$
$\quad 3x + y = -23$

19. $2x + 2y = 7$
$\quad x - 2y = -1$

20. $2.5x + y = -2$
$\quad 3x + 2y = 0$

5-2 Practice

Substitution

Use substitution to solve each system of equations. If the system does *not* have exactly one solution, state whether it has *no* solution or *infinitely many* solutions.

1. $y = 6x$
$2x + 3y = -20$

2. $x = 3y$
$3x - 5y = 12$

3. $x = 2y + 7$
$x = y + 4$

4. $y = 2x - 2$
$y = x + 2$

5. $y = 2x + 6$
$2x - y = 2$

6. $3x + y = 12$
$y = -x - 2$

7. $x + 2y = 13$
$-2x - 3y = -18$

8. $x - 2y = 3$
$4x - 8y = 12$

9. $x - 5y = 36$
$2x + y = -16$

10. $2x - 3y = -24$
$x + 6y = 18$

11. $x + 14y = 84$
$2x - 7y = -7$

12. $0.3x - 0.2y = 0.5$
$x - 2y = -5$

13. $0.5x + 4y = -1$
$x + 2.5y = 3.5$

14. $3x - 2y = 11$
$x - \frac{1}{2}y = 4$

15. $\frac{1}{2}x + 2y = 12$
$x - 2y = 6$

16. $\frac{1}{3}x - y = 3$
$2x + y = 25$

17. $4x - 5y = -7$
$y = 5x$

18. $x - 3y = -4$
$2x + 6y = 5$

EMPLOYMENT For Exercises 19–21, use the following information.

Kenisha sells athletic shoes part-time at a department store. She can earn either $500 per month plus a 4% commission on her total sales, or $400 per month plus a 5% commission on total sales.

19. Write a system of equations to represent the situation.

20. What is the total price of the athletic shoes Kenisha needs to sell to earn the same income from each pay scale?

21. Which is the better offer?

MOVIE TICKETS For Exercises 22 and 23, use the following information.

Tickets to a movie cost $7.25 for adults and $5.50 for students. A group of friends purchased 8 tickets for $52.75.

22. Write a system of equations to represent the situation.

23. How many adult tickets and student tickets were purchased?

5-2 Word Problem Practice

Substitution

1. BUSINESS Mr. Randolph finds that the supply and demand for gasoline at his station are generally given by the following equations.

$$x - y = -2$$
$$x + y = 10$$

Use substitution to find the equilibrium point where the supply and demand lines intersect.

2. GEOMETRY The measures of complementary angles have a sum of 90 degrees. Angle A and angle B are complementary, and their measures have a difference of 20°. What are the measures of the angles?

3. MONEY Harvey has some $1 bills and some $5 bills. In all, he has 6 bills worth $22. Let x be the number of $1 bills and let y be the number of $5 bills. Write a system of equations to represent the information and use substitution to determine how many bills of each denomination Harvey has.

4. POPULATION Sanjay is researching population trends in South America. He found that experts expect the population of Ecuador to increase by 1,000,000 and the population of Chile to increase by 600,000 from 2004 to 2009. The table displays the information he found.

Country	2004 Population	Predicted 5-Year Change
Ecuador	13,000,000	+1,000,000
Chile	16,000,000	+600,000

Source: *World Almanac 2005*

If the population growth for each country continues at the same rate, in what year are the populations of Ecuador and Chile predicted to be equal?

CHEMISTRY For Exercises 5 and 6, use the following information.

Shelby and Calvin are doing a chemistry experiment. They need 5 ounces of a solution that is 65% acid and 35% distilled water. There is no undiluted acid in the chemistry lab, but they do have two flasks of diluted acid: Flask A contains 70% acid and 30% distilled water. Flask B contains 20% acid and 80% distilled water.

5. Write a system of equations that Shelby and Calvin could use to determine how many ounces they need to pour from each flask to make their solution.

6. Solve your system of equations. How many ounces from each flask do Shelby and Calvin need?

5-2 **Enrichment**

Intersection of Two Parabolas

Substitution can be used to find the intersection of two parabolas. Replace the *y*-value in one of the equations with the *y*-value in terms of *x* from the other equation.

Example Find the intersection of the two parabolas.

$$y = x^2 + 5x + 6$$
$$y = x^2 + 4x + 3$$

Graph the equations.

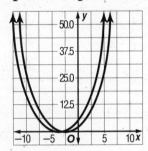

From the graph, notice that the two graphs intersect in one point.

Use substitution to solve for the point of intersection.

$x^2 + 5x + 6 = x^2 + 4x + 3$	
$5x + 6 = 4x + 3$	Subtract x^2 from both sides.
$x + 6 = 3$	Subtract $4x$ from both sides.
$x = -3$	Subtract 6 from both sides.

So, the graphs intersect at $x = -3$.

Replace *x* with -3 in either equation to find the *y*-value.

$y = x^2 + 5x + 6$	Original equation
$y = (-3)2 + 5(-3) + 6$	Replace *x* with -3.
$y = 9 - 15 + 6 \ or \ 0.$	Simplify.

So, the point of intersection is $(-3, 0)$

Exercises

Use substitution to find the point of intersection of the graphs of each pair of equations.

1. $y = x^2 + 8x + 7$
   $y = x^2 + 2x + 1$

2. $y = x^2 + 6x + 8$
   $y = x^2 + 4x + 4$

3. $y = x^2 + 5x + 6$
   $y = x^2 + 7x + 6$

Lesson 5-2

5-3 Lesson Reading Guide

Elimination Using Addition and Subtraction

Get Ready for the Lesson

Read the introduction to Lesson 5-3 in your textbook.

What fact explains why the variable d gets eliminated from the system of equations?

Read the Lesson

1. Write *addition* or *subtraction* to tell which operation it would be easiest to use to eliminate a variable of the system. Explain your choice.

	System of Equations	Operation	Explanation
a.	$3x + 5y = 12$ $-3x + 2y = 6$		
b.	$3x + 5y = 7$ $3x - 2y = 8$		
c.	$-x - 4y = 9$ $4x - 4y = 6$		
d.	$5x - 7y = 17$ $8x + 7y = 9$		

Remember What You Learned

2. Tell how you can decide whether to use addition or subtraction to eliminate a variable in a system of equations.

5-3 Study Guide and Intervention

Elimination Using Addition and Subtraction

Elimination Using Addition In systems of equations in which the coefficients of the x or y terms are additive inverses, solve the system by adding the equations. Because one of the variables is eliminated, this method is called **elimination**.

Example 1 Use addition to solve the system of equations.
$x - 3y = 7$
$3x + 3y = 9$

Write the equations in column form and add to eliminate y.

$$\begin{array}{r} x - 3y = 7 \\ (+)\ 3x + 3y = 9 \\ \hline 4x = 16 \end{array}$$

Solve for x.

$$\frac{4x}{4} = \frac{16}{4}$$
$$x = 4$$

Substitute 4 for x in either equation and solve for y.

$$4 - 3y = 7$$
$$4 - 3y - 4 = 7 - 4$$
$$-3y = 3$$
$$\frac{-3y}{-3} = \frac{3}{-3}$$
$$y = -1$$

The solution is $(4, -1)$.

Example 2 The sum of two numbers is 70 and their difference is 24. Find the numbers.

Let x represent one number and y represent the other number.

$$\begin{array}{r} x + y = 70 \\ (+)\ x - y = 24 \\ \hline 2x = 94 \end{array}$$
$$\frac{2x}{2} = \frac{94}{2}$$
$$x = 47$$

Substitute 47 for x in either equation.

$$47 + y = 70$$
$$47 + y - 47 = 70 - 47$$
$$y = 23$$

The numbers are 47 and 23.

Exercises

Use elimination to solve each system of equations.

1. $x + y = -4$
   $x - y = 2$

2. $2m - 3n = 14$
   $m + 3n = -11$

3. $3a - b = -9$
   $-3a - 2b = 0$

4. $-3x - 4y = -1$
   $3x - y = -4$

5. $3c + d = 4$
   $2c - d = 6$

6. $-2x + 2y = 9$
   $2x - y = -6$

7. $2x + 2y = -2$
   $3x - 2y = 12$

8. $4x - 2y = -1$
   $-4x + 4y = -2$

9. $x - y = 2$
   $x + y = -3$

10. $2x - 3y = 12$
    $4x + 3y = 24$

11. $-0.2x + y = 0.5$
    $0.2x + 2y = 1.6$

12. $0.1x + 0.3y = 0.9$
    $0.1x - 0.3y = 0.2$

13. Rema is older than Ken. The difference of their ages is 12 and the sum of their ages is 50. Find the age of each.

14. The sum of the digits of a two-digit number is 12. The difference of the digits is 2. Find the number if the units digit is larger than the tens digit.

21

5-3 Study Guide and Intervention *(continued)*

Elimination Using Addition and Subtraction

Elimination Using Subtraction In systems of equations where the coefficients of the x or y terms are the same, solve the system by subtracting the equations.

Example Use subtraction to solve the system of equations.

$2x - 3y = 11$
$5x - 3y = 14$

$$\begin{array}{r} 2x - 3y = 11 \\ (-)\ 5x - 3y = 14 \\ \hline -3x = -3 \end{array}$$ Write the equations in column form and subtract.

Subtract the two equations. y is eliminated.

$\dfrac{-3x}{-3} = \dfrac{-3}{-3}$ Divide each side by -3.

$x = 1$ Simplify.

$2(1) - 3y = 11$ Substitute 1 for x in either equation.
$2 - 3y = 11$ Simplify.
$2 - 3y - 2 = 11 - 2$ Subtract 2 from each side.
$-3y = 9$ Simplify.
$\dfrac{-3y}{-3} = \dfrac{9}{-3}$ Divide each side by -3.
$y = -3$ Simplify.

The solution is $(1, -3)$.

Exercises

Use elimination to solve each system of equations.

1. $6x + 5y = 4$
$6x - 7y = -20$

2. $3m - 4n = -14$
$3m + 2n = -2$

3. $3a + b = 1$
$a + b = 3$

4. $-3x - 4y = -23$
$-3x + y = 2$

5. $c - 3d = 11$
$2c - 3d = 16$

6. $x - 2y = 6$
$x + y = 3$

7. $2a - 3b = -13$
$2a + 2b = 7$

8. $4x + 2y = 6$
$4x + 4y = 10$

9. $5s - t = 6$
$5s + 2t = 3$

10. $6x - 3y = 12$
$4x - 3y = 24$

11. $x + 2y = 3.5$
$x - 3y = -9$

12. $0.2x + y = 0.7$
$0.2x + 2y = 1.2$

13. The sum of two numbers is 70. One number is ten more than twice the other number. Find the numbers.

14. GEOMETRY Two angles are supplementary. The measure of one angle is 10° more than three times the other. Find the measure of each angle.

5-3 Skills Practice

Elimination Using Addition and Subtraction

Use elimination to solve each system of equations.

1. $x - y = 1$
   $x + y = 3$

2. $-x + y = 1$
   $x + y = 11$

3. $x + 4y = 11$
   $x - 6y = 11$

4. $-x + 3y = 6$
   $x + 3y = 18$

5. $3x + 4y = 19$
   $3x + 6y = 33$

6. $x + 4y = -8$
   $x - 4y = -8$

7. $3a + 4b = 2$
   $4a - 4b = 12$

8. $3c - d = -1$
   $-3c - d = 5$

9. $2x - 3y = 9$
   $-5x - 3y = 30$

10. $x - y = 4$
    $2x + y = -4$

11. $3m - n = 26$
    $-2m - n = -24$

12. $5x - y = -6$
    $-x + y = 2$

13. $6x - 2y = 32$
    $4x - 2y = 18$

14. $3x + 2y = -19$
    $-3x - 5y = 25$

15. $7m + 4n = 2$
    $7m + 2n = 8$

16. $2x - 5y = -28$
    $4x + 5y = 4$

17. The sum of two numbers is 28 and their difference is 4. What are the numbers?

18. Find the two numbers whose sum is 29 and whose difference is 15.

19. The sum of two numbers is 24 and their difference is 2. What are the numbers?

20. Find the two numbers whose sum is 54 and whose difference is 4.

21. Two times a number added to another number is 25. Three times the first number minus the other number is 20. Find the numbers.

Lesson 5-3

5-3 Practice

Elimination Using Addition and Subtraction

Use elimination to solve each system of equations.

1. $x - y = 1$
   $x + y = -9$

2. $p + q = -2$
   $p - q = 8$

3. $4x + y = 23$
   $3x - y = 12$

4. $2x + 5y = -3$
   $2x + 2y = 6$

5. $3x + 2y = -1$
   $4x + 2y = -6$

6. $5x + 3y = 22$
   $5x - 2y = 2$

7. $5x + 2y = 7$
   $-2x + 2y = -14$

8. $3x - 9y = -12$
   $3x - 15y = -6$

9. $-4c - 2d = -2$
   $2c - 2d = -14$

10. $2x - 6y = 6$
    $2x + 3y = 24$

11. $7x + 2y = 2$
    $7x - 2y = -30$

12. $4.25x - 1.28y = -9.2$
    $x + 1.28y = 17.6$

13. $2x + 4y = 10$
    $x - 4y = -2.5$

14. $2.5x + y = 10.7$
    $2.5x + 2y = 12.9$

15. $6m - 8n = 3$
    $2m - 8n = -3$

16. $4a + b = 2$
    $4a + 3b = 10$

17. $-\frac{1}{3}x - \frac{4}{3}y = -2$
    $\frac{1}{3}x - \frac{2}{3}y = 4$

18. $\frac{3}{4}x - \frac{1}{2}y = 8$
    $\frac{3}{2}x + \frac{1}{2}y = 19$

19. The sum of two numbers is 41 and their difference is 5. What are the numbers?

20. Four times one number added to another number is 36. Three times the first number minus the other number is 20. Find the numbers.

21. One number added to three times another number is 24. Five times the first number added to three times the other number is 36. Find the numbers.

22. **LANGUAGES** English is spoken as the first or primary language in 78 more countries than Farsi is spoken as the first language. Together, English and Farsi are spoken as a first language in 130 countries. In how many countries is English spoken as the first language? In how many countries is Farsi spoken as the first language?

23. **DISCOUNTS** At a sale on winter clothing, Cody bought two pairs of gloves and four hats for $43.00. Tori bought two pairs of gloves and two hats for $30.00. What were the prices for the gloves and hats?

5-3 Word Problem Practice

Elimination Using Addition and Subtraction

1. NUMBER FUN Ms. Simms, the sixth grade math teacher, gave her students this challenge problem.

> Twice a number added to another number is 15. The sum of the two numbers is 11.

Lorenzo, an algebra student who was Ms. Simms aide, realized he could solve the problem by writing the following equations.

$$2x + y = 15$$
$$x + y = 11$$

Use the elimination method to solve the system and find the two numbers.

2. GOVERNMENT The Texas State Legislature is comprised of state senators and state representatives. The sum of the number of senators and representatives is 181. There are 119 more representatives than senators. How many senators and how many representatives make up the Texas Legislature?

3. RESEARCH Melissa wondered how much it cost to send a letter by mail in 1990, so she asked her father. Rather than answer directly, Melissa's father gave her the following information. It would have cost $3.70 to send 13 postcards and 7 letters, and it would have cost $2.65 to send 6 postcards and 7 letters. Use a system of equations and elimination to find how much it cost to send a letter in 1990.

4. SPORTS As of 2004 the New York Yankees had won more Major League Baseball World Series than any other team. In fact The Yankees had won 1 fewer than 3 times the number of World Series won by the Oakland A's. The sum of the two teams' World Series championships is 35. How many times has each team won the World Series has each team?

BASKETBALL For Exercises 5 and 6, use the following information.

In 2005, the average ticket prices for Dallas Mavericks games and Boston Celtics games are shown in the table below. The change in price is from the 2004 season to the 2005 season.

Team	Average Ticket Price	Change in Price
Dallas	$53.60	$0.53
Boston	$55.93	−$1.08

Source: TeamMarketingReport.com

5. Assume that tickets continue to change at the same rate each year after 2005. Let x be the number of years after 2005, and y be the price of an average ticket. Write a system of equations to represent the information in the table.

6. In how many years will the average ticket price for Dallas approximately equal that of Boston?

Lesson 5-3

5-3 Enrichment

Solving Systems of Equations in Three Variables

Systems of equations can involve more than 2 equations and 2 variables. It is possible to solve a system of 3 equations and 3 variables using elimination.

Example Solve the following system.

$$x + y + z = 6$$
$$3x - y + z = 8$$
$$x - z = 2$$

Step 1: Use elimination to get rid of the y in the first two equations.

$$\begin{array}{r} x + y + z = 6 \\ 3x - y + z = 8 \\ \hline 4x + 2z = 14 \end{array}$$

Step 2: Use the equation you found in step 1 and the third equation to eliminate the z.

$$4x + 2z = 14$$
$$x - z = 2$$

Multiply the second equation by 2 so that the z's will eliminate.

$$\begin{array}{r} 4x + 2z = 14 \\ 2x - 2z = 4 \\ \hline 6x = 18 \end{array}$$

So, $x = 3$.

Step 3: Replace x with 3 in the third original equation to determine z.

$3 - z = 2$, so $z = 1$.

Step 4: Replace x with 3 and z with 1 in either of the first two original equation to determine the value of y.

$3 + y + 1 = 6$ or $4 + y = 6$.   So, $y = 2$.

So, the solution to the system of equations is $(3, 2, 1)$.

Exercises Solve each system of equations.

1. $3x + 2y + z = 42$
   $2y + z + 12 = 3x$
   $x - 3y = 0$

2. $x + y + z = -3$
   $2x + 3y + 5z = -4$
   $2y - z = 4$

3. $x + y + z = 7$
   $x + 2y + z = 10$
   $2y + z = 5$

5-4 Lesson Reading Guide
Elimination Using Multiplication

Get Ready for the Lesson

Read the introduction to Lesson 5-4 in your textbook.

Can the system of equations be solved by elimination with addition or subtraction? Explain.

Reading the Lesson

1. Could elimination by multiplication be used to solve the system shown below? Explain.
   $3x - 5y = 15$
   $-6x + 7y = 11$

2. Tell whether it would be easiest to use substitution, elimination by addition, elimination by subtraction, or elimination by multiplication to solve the system. Explain your choice.

	System of Equations	Solution Method	Explanation
a.	$-3x + 4y = 2$ $3x + 2y = 10$		
b.	$x - 2y = 0$ $5x - 4y = 8$		
c.	$6x - 5y = -18$ $2x + 10y = 27$		
d.	$-2x + 3y = 9$ $3x + 3y = 12$		

Remember What You Learned

3. If you are going to solve a system by elimination, how do you decide whether you will need to multiply one or both equations by a number?

Lesson 5-4

5-4 Study Guide and Intervention

Elimination Using Multiplication

Elimination Using Multiplication Some systems of equations cannot be solved simply by adding or subtracting the equations. In such cases, one or both equations must first be multiplied by a number before the system can be solved by elimination.

Example 1 Use elimination to solve the system of equations.

$x + 10y = 3$
$4x + 5y = 5$

If you multiply the second equation by -2, you can eliminate the y terms.

$$\begin{array}{r} x + 10y = 3 \\ (+) \; -8x - 10y = -10 \\ \hline -7x \quad\quad = -7 \end{array}$$

$$\frac{-7x}{-7} = \frac{-7}{-7}$$

$$x = 1$$

Substitute 1 for x in either equation.

$$1 + 10y = 3$$
$$1 + 10y - 1 = 3 - 1$$
$$10y = 2$$
$$\frac{10y}{10} = \frac{2}{10}$$
$$y = \frac{1}{5}$$

The solution is $\left(1, \dfrac{1}{5}\right)$.

Example 2 Use elimination to solve the system of equations.

$3x - 2y = -7$
$2x - 5y = 10$

If you multiply the first equation by 2 and the second equation by -3, you can eliminate the x terms.

$$\begin{array}{r} 6x - 4y = -14 \\ (+) \; -6x + 15y = -30 \\ \hline 11y = -44 \end{array}$$

$$\frac{11y}{11} = \frac{-44}{11}$$

$$y = -4$$

Substitute -4 for y in either equation.

$$3x - 2(-4) = -7$$
$$3x + 8 = -7$$
$$3x + 8 - 8 = -7 - 8$$
$$3x = -15$$
$$\frac{3x}{3} = \frac{-15}{3}$$
$$x = -5$$

The solution is $(-5, -4)$.

Exercises

Use elimination to solve each system of equations.

1. $2x + 3y = 6$
$x + 2y = 5$

2. $2m + 3n = 4$
$-m + 2n = 5$

3. $3a - b = 2$
$a + 2b = 3$

4. $4x + 5y = 6$
$6x - 7y = -20$

5. $4c - 3d = 22$
$2c - d = 10$

6. $3x - 4y = -4$
$x + 3y = -10$

7. $4s - t = 9$
$5s + 2t = 8$

8. $4a - 3b = -8$
$2a + 2b = 3$

9. $2x + 2y = 5$
$4x - 4y = 10$

10. $6x - 4y = -8$
$4x + 2y = -3$

11. $4x + 2y = -5$
$-2x - 4y = 1$

12. $2x + y = 3.5$
$-x + 2y = 2.5$

13. GARDENING The length of Sally's garden is 4 meters greater than 3 times the width. The perimeter of her garden is 72 meters. What are the dimensions of Sally's garden?

14. Anita is $4\dfrac{1}{2}$ years older than Basilio. Three times Anita's age added to six times Basilio's age is 36. How old are Anita and Basilio?

5-4 Study Guide and Intervention *(continued)*

Elimination Using Multiplication

Determine the Best Method The methods to use for solving systems of linear equations are summarized in the table below.

Method	The Best Time to Use
Graphing	to estimate the solution, since graphing usually does not give an exact solution
Substitution	if one of the variables in either equation has a coefficient of 1 or -1
Elimination Using Addition	if one of the variables has opposite coefficients in the two equations
Elimination Using Subtraction	if one of the variables has the same coefficient in the two equations
Elimination Using Multiplication	if none of the coefficients are 1 or -1 and neither of the variables can be eliminated by simply adding or subtracting the equations

Example Determine the best method to solve the system of equations. Then solve the system.

$$6x + 2y = 20$$
$$-2x + 4y = -16$$

Since the coefficients of x will be additive inverses of each other if you multiply the second equation by 3, use elimination.

$$\begin{array}{ll} 6x + 2y = 20 & \\ (+) \ -6x + 12y = -48 & \text{Multiply the second equation by 3.} \\ \hline 14y = -28 & \text{Add the two equations. } x \text{ is eliminated.} \\ \dfrac{14y}{14} = \dfrac{-28}{14} & \text{Divide each side by 14.} \\ y = -2 & \text{Simplify.} \end{array}$$

$$\begin{array}{ll} 6x + 2(-2) = 20 & \text{Substitute } -2 \text{ for } y \text{ in either equation.} \\ 6x - 4 = 20 & \text{Simplify.} \\ 6x - 4 + 4 = 20 + 4 & \text{Add 4 to each side.} \\ 6x = 24 & \text{Simplify.} \\ \dfrac{6x}{6} = \dfrac{24}{6} & \text{Divide each side by 6.} \\ x = 4 & \text{Simplify.} \end{array}$$

The solution is $(4, -2)$.

Exercises

Determine the best method to solve each system of equations. Then solve the system.

1. $x + 2y = 3$
   $x + y = 1$

2. $m + 6n = -8$
   $m = 2n + 8$

3. $a - b = 6$
   $a = 2b + 7$

4. $4x + y = 15$
   $-x - 3y = -12$

5. $3c - d = 14$
   $c - d = 2$

6. $x + 2y = -9$
   $y = 4x$

7. $4x = 2y - 10$
   $x + 2y = 5$

8. $x = -2y$
   $4x + 4y = -10$

9. $2s - 3t = 42$
   $3s + 2t = 24$

10. $4a - 4b = -10$
   $2a + 4b = -2$

11. $4x + 10y = -6$
   $-2x - 10y = 2$

12. $2x = y - 3$
   $-x + y = 0$

Lesson 5-4

5-4 Skills Practice

Elimination Using Multiplication

Use elimination to solve each system of equations.

1. $x + y = -9$
   $5x - 2y = 32$

2. $3x + 2y = -9$
   $x - y = -13$

3. $2x + 5y = 3$
   $-x + 3y = -7$

4. $2x + y = 3$
   $-4x - 4y = -8$

5. $4x - 2y = -14$
   $3x - y = -8$

6. $2x + y = 0$
   $5x + 3y = 2$

7. $5x + 3y = -10$
   $3x + 5y = -6$

8. $2x + 3y = 14$
   $3x - 4y = 4$

9. $2x - 3y = 21$
   $5x - 2y = 25$

10. $3x + 2y = -26$
    $4x - 5y = -4$

11. $3x - 6y = -3$
    $2x + 4y = 30$

12. $5x + 2y = -3$
    $3x + 3y = 9$

13. Two times a number plus three times another number equals 13. The sum of the two numbers is 7. What are the numbers?

14. Four times a number minus twice another number is -16. The sum of the two numbers is -1. Find the numbers.

Determine the best method to solve each system of equations. Then solve the system.

15. $2x + 3y = 10$
    $5x + 2y = -8$

16. $8x - 7y = 18$
    $3x + 7y = 26$

17. $y = 2x$
    $3x + 2y = 35$

18. $3x + y = 6$
    $3x + y = 3$

19. $3x - 4y = 17$
    $4x + 5y = 2$

20. $y = 3x + 1$
    $3x - y = -1$

5-4 Practice

Elimination Using Multiplication

Use elimination to solve each system of equations.

1. $2x - y = -1$
$3x - 2y = 1$

2. $5x - 2y = -10$
$3x + 6y = 66$

3. $7x + 4y = -4$
$5x + 8y = 28$

4. $2x - 4y = -22$
$3x + 3y = 30$

5. $3x + 2y = -9$
$5x - 3y = 4$

6. $4x - 2y = 32$
$-3x - 5y = -11$

7. $3x + 4y = 27$
$5x - 3y = 16$

8. $0.5x + 0.5y = -2$
$x - 0.25y = 6$

9. $2x - \dfrac{3}{4}y = -7$

$x + \dfrac{1}{2}y = 0$

10. Eight times a number plus five times another number is -13. The sum of the two numbers is 1. What are the numbers?

11. Two times a number plus three times another number equals 4. Three times the first number plus four times the other number is 7. Find the numbers.

Determine the best method to solve each system of equations. Then solve the system.

12. $5x + 7y = 3$
$2x - 7y = -38$

13. $7x + 2y = 2$
$2x - 3y = -28$

14. $-6x - 2y = 14$
$6x + 8y = -20$

15. $x = 2y + 6$
$\dfrac{1}{2}x - y = 3$

16. $4x + 3y = -2$
$4x + 3y = 3$

17. $y = \dfrac{1}{2}x$

$\dfrac{5}{2}x - 2y = 9$

18. FINANCE Gunther invested \$10,000 in two mutual funds. One of the funds rose 6% in one year, and the other rose 9% in one year. If Gunther's investment rose a total of \$684 in one year, how much did he invest in each mutual fund?

19. CANOEING Laura and Brent paddled a canoe 6 miles upstream in four hours. The return trip took three hours. Find the rate at which Laura and Brent paddled the canoe in still water.

20. NUMBER THEORY The sum of the digits of a two-digit number is 11. If the digits are reversed, the new number is 45 more than the original number. Find the number.

Lesson 5-4

5-4 Word Problem Practice

Elimination Using Multiplication

1. SOCCER Suppose a youth soccer field has a perimeter of 320 yards and its length measures 40 yards more than its width. Ms. Hughey asks her players to determine the length and width of their field. She gives them the following system of equations to represent the situation. Use elimination to solve the system to find the length and width of the field.

$$2L + 2W = 320$$
$$L - W = 40$$

2. SPORTS The Fan Cost Index (FCI) tracks the average costs for attending sporting events, including tickets, drinks, food, parking, programs, and souvenirs. According to the FCI, a family of four would spend a total of $592.30 to attend two Major League Baseball (MLB) games and one National Basketball Association (NBA) game. The family would spend $691.31 to attend one MLB and two NBA games. Write and solve a system of equations to find the family's costs for each kind of game according to the FCI.

3. ART Mr. Santos, the curator of the children's museum, recently made two purchases of clay and wood for a visiting artist to sculpt. Use the table to find the cost of each product per kilogram.

Clay (kg)	Wood (kg)	Total Cost
5	4	$35.50
3.5	6	$50.45

4. TRAVEL Antonio flies from Houston to Philadelphia, a distance of about 1340 miles. His plane travels with the wind and takes 2 hours and 20 minutes. At the same time, Paul is on a plane from Philadelphia to Houston. Since his plane is heading against the wind, Paul's flight takes 2 hours and 50 minutes. What was the speed of the wind in miles per hour?

BUSINESS For Exercises 5–7, use the following information.

Suppose you start a business assembling and selling motorized scooters. It costs you $1500 for tools and equipment to get started, and the materials cost $200 for each scooter. Your scooters sell for $300 each.

5. Write and solve a system of equations representing the total costs and revenue of your business.

6. Describe what the solution means in terms of the situation.

7. Give an example of a reasonable number of scooters you could assemble and sell in order to make a profit, and find the profit you would make for that number of scooters.

5-4 Enrichment

George Washington Carver and Percy Julian

In 1990, George Washington Carver and Percy Julian became the first African Americans elected to the National Inventors Hall of Fame. Carver (1864–1943) was an agricultural scientist known worldwide for developing hundreds of uses for the peanut and the sweet potato. His work revitalized the economy of the southern United States because it was no longer dependent solely upon cotton. Julian (1898–1975) was a research chemist who became famous for inventing a method of making a synthetic cortisone from soybeans. His discovery has had many medical applications, particularly in the treatment of arthritis.

There are dozens of other African American inventors whose accomplishments are not as well known. Their inventions range from common household items like the ironing board to complex devices that have revolutionized manufacturing. The exercises that follow will help you identify just a few of these inventors and their inventions.

Match the inventors with their inventions by matching each system with its solution. (Not all the solutions will be used.)

1. Sara Boone
$x + y = 2$
$x - y = 10$

A. $(1, 4)$ automatic traffic signal

2. Sarah Goode
$x = 2 - y$
$2y + x = 9$

B. $(4, -2)$ eggbeater

3. Frederick M. Jones
$y = 2x + 6$
$y = -x - 3$

C. $(-2, 3)$ fire extinguisher

4. J. L. Love
$2x + 3y = 8$
$2x - y = -8$

D. $(-5, 7)$ folding cabinet bed

5. T. J. Marshall
$y - 3x = 9$
$2y + x = 4$

E. $(6, -4)$ ironing board

6. Jan Matzeliger
$y + 4 = 2x$
$6x - 3y = 12$

F. $(-2, 4)$ pencil sharpener

7. Garrett A. Morgan
$3x - 2y = -5$
$3y - 4x = 8$

G. $(-3, 0)$ portable X-ray machine

8. Norbert Rillieux
$3x - y = 12$
$y - 3x = 15$

H. $(2, -3)$ player piano

I. no solution   evaporating pan for refining sugar

J. infinitely many solutions   lasting (shaping) machine for manufacturing shoes

Lesson 5-4

5-5 Lesson Reading Guide

Applying Systems of Linear Equations

Get Ready For the Lesson

Do the activity at the beginning of the lesson in your textbook.

  a. Write an equation to describe the total length of both tours.

  b. Write an equation to describe the relationship between the length of the Crystal Palace tour and then Horseshoe Lake tour.

  c. Combine both equations into a system of equations. Use any method to solve for the lengths of the tours.

Read the Lesson

Complete the following chart.

Method	The Best Time to Use
Graphing	
Substitution	
Elimination Using Addition	
Elimination Using Subtraction	
Elimination Using Multiplication	

Remember What You Learned

7. Think of an example of a system of linear equations you have seen earlier in this lesson. Explain what the benefits or drawbacks might be for using each of the methods for solving systems of linear equations.

5-5 Study Guide and Intervention

Applying Systems of Linear Equations

DETERMINE THE BEST METHOD   You have learned five methods for solving systems of linear equations: graphing, substitution, elimination using addition, elimination using subtraction, and elimination using multiplication. For an exact solution, an algebraic method is best.

Example   At a baseball game, Henry bought 3 hotdogs and a bag of chips for $14. Scott bought 2 hotdogs and a bag of chips for $10. The hotdogs and chips were all the same price, so the following system of equations can be used to represent the situation. Determine the best method to solving the system of equations. Then solve the system.

$3x + y = 14$
$2x + y = 10$

- Since neither the coefficients of x nor the coefficients of y are additive inverses, you cannot use elimination using addition.

- Since the coefficient of y in both equations is 1, you can use elimination using subtraction. You could also use the substitution method or elimination using multiplication

The following solution uses elimination by subtraction to solve this system.

$$\begin{array}{rl} 3x + \quad y = \quad 14 & \text{Write the equations in column form and subtract.} \\ \underline{(-)\, 2x + (-)\, y = (-)10} & \\ x \quad\quad = \quad 4 & \text{The variable } y \text{ is eliminated.} \\ 3(4) + \quad y = \quad 14 & \text{Substitute the value for } x \text{ back into the first equation.} \\ y = \quad 2 & \text{Solve for } y. \end{array}$$

This means that hot dogs cost $4 each and a bag of chips costs $2.

Exercises

Determine the best method to solve each system of equations. Then solve the system.

1. $5x + 3y = 16$
   $3x - 5y = -4$

2. $3x - 5y = 7$
   $2x + 5y = 13$

3. $y + 3x = 24$
   $5x - y = 8$

4. $-11x - 10y = 17$
   $5x - 7y = 50$

Lesson 5-5

5-5 Study Guide and Intervention *(continued)*

Applying Systems of Linear Equations

APPLY SYSTEMS OF LINEAR EQUATIONS   When applying systems of linear equations to problem situations, it is important to analyze each solution in the context of the situation.

Example   **BUSINESS**   A T-shirt printing company sells T-shirt for $15 each. The company has a fixed cost for the machine used to print the T-shirts and an additional cost per T-shirt. Use the table to estimate the number of T-shirts the company must sell in order for the income equal to expenses.

T-shirt Printing Cost	
Printing machine	$3000.00
blank T-shirt	$5.00

Explore   You know the initial income and the initial expense and the rates of change of each quantity with each T-shirt sold.

Plan   Write an equation to represent the income and the expenses. Then solve to find how many T-shirts need to be sold for both values to be equal.

Solve   Let x = the number of T-shirts sold and let y = the total amount.

total amount	initial amount	rate of change times number of T-shirts sold

income $y = 0 + 15x$

expenses $y = 3000 + 5x$

You can use substitution to solve this system.

$y = 15x$ The first equation.

$15x = 3000 + 5x$ Substitute the value for y into the second equation.

$10x = 3000$ Subtract 10x from each side and simplify.

$x = 300$ Divide each side by 10 and simplify.

This means that if 300 T-shirts are sold, the income and expenses of the T-shirt company are equal.

Check   Does this solution make sense in the context of the problem? After selling 100 T-shirts, the income would be about 100 × $15 or $1500. The costs would be about $3000 + 100 × $5 or $3500.

Exercises

Refer to the example above. If the costs of the T-shirt company change to the given values and the selling price remains the same, determine the number of T-shirts the company must sell in order for income to equal expenses.

1. printing machine: $5000.00; T-shirt: $10.00 each

2. printing machine: $2100.00; T-shirt: $8.00 each

3. printing machine: $8800.00; T-shirt: $4.00 each

4. printing machine: $1200.00; T-shirt: $12.00 each

5-5 Skills Practice

Applying Systems of Linear Equations

Determine the best method to solve each system of equations. Then solve the system.

1. $5x + 3y = 16$
  $3x - 5y = -4$

2. $3x - 5y = 7$
  $2x + 5y = 13$

3. $y = 3x - 24$
  $5x - y = 8$

4. $-11x - 10y = 17$
  $5x - 7y = 50$

5. $4x + y = 24$
  $5x - y = 12$

6. $6x - y = -145$
  $x = 4 - 2y$

7. VEGETABLE STAND A roadside vegetable stand sells pumpkins for $5 each and squashes for $3 each. One day they sold 6 more squash than pumpkins, and their sales totaled $98. Write and solve a system of equations to find how many pumpkins and squash they sold?

8. INCOME Ramiro earns $20 per hour during the week and $30 per hour for overtime on the weekends. One week Ramiro earned a total of $650. He worked 5 times as many hours during the week as he did on the weekend. Write and solve a system of equations to determine how many hours of overtime Ramiro worked on the weekend.

9. BASKETBALL Anya makes 14 baskets during her game. Some of these baskets were worth 2-points and others were worth 3-points. In total, she scored 30 points. Write and solve a system of equations to find how 2-points baskets she made.

Lesson 5-5

5-5 Practice

Applying systems of Linear Equations

Determine the best method to solve each system of equations. Then solve the system.

1. $1.5x - 1.9y = -29$
$x - 0.9y = 4.5$

2. $1.2x - 0.8y = -6$
$4.8x + 2.4y = 60$

3. $18x - 16y = -312$
$78x - 16y = 408$

4. $14x + 7y = 217$
$14x + 3y = 189$

5. $x = 3.6y + 0.7$
$2x + 0.2y = 38.4$

6. $5.3x - 4y = 43.5$
$x + 7y = 78$

7. BOOKS A library contains 2000 books. There are 3 times as many non-fiction books as fiction books. Write and solve a system of equations to determine the number of non-fiction and fiction books.

8. SCHOOL CLUBS The chess club has 16 members and gains a new member every month. The film club has 4 members and gains 4 new members every month. Write and solve a system of equations to find when the number of members in both clubs will be equal.

For Exercises 9 and 10, use the information below.

Tia and Ken each sold snack bars and magazine subscriptions for a school fund-raiser, as shown in the table. Tia earned $132 and Ken earned $190.

Item	Number Sold	
	Tia	Ken
snack bars	16	20
magazine subscriptions	4	6

9. Define variable and formulate a system of linear equation from this situation.

10. What was the price per snack bar? Determine the reasonableness of your solution.

5-5 Word Problem Practice

Applying Systems of Linear Equations

1. **MONEY** Veronica has been saving dimes and quarters. She has 94 coins in all, and the total value is $19.30. How many dimes and how many quarters does she have?

2. **CHEMISTRY** How many liters of 15% acid and 33% acid should be mixed to make 40 liters of 21% acid solution?

Concentration of Solution	Amount of Solution (L)	Amount of Acid
15%	x	
33%	y	
21%	40	

3. **BUILDINGS** The Sears Tower in Chicago is the tallest building in North America. The total height of the tower t and the antenna that stands on top of it a is 1729 feet. The difference in heights between the building and the antenna is 1171 feet. How tall is the Sears Tower?

4. **PRODUCE** Roger and Trevor went shopping for produce on the same day. They each bought some apples and some potatoes. The amount they bought and the total price they paid are listed in the table below.

	Apples (lb)	Potatoes (lb)	Total Cost ($)
Roger	8	7	18.85
Trevor	2	10	12.88

What was the price of apples and potatoes per pound?

5. **SHOPPING** Two stores are having a sale on T-shirts that normally sell for $20. Store S is advertising an s percent discount, and Store T is advertising a t dollar discount. Rose spends $63 for three T-shirts from Store S and one from Store T. Manny spends $140 on five T-shirts from Store S and four from Store T. Find the discount at each store.

TRANSPORTATION For Exercises 6–8 use the following information.

A Speedy River barge bound for New Orleans leaves Baton Rouge, Louisiana, at 9:00 A.M. and travels at a speed of 10 miles per hour. A Rail Transport freight train also bound for New Orleans leaves Baton Rouge at 1:30 P.M. the same day. The train travels at 25 miles per hour, and the river barge travels at 10 miles per hour. Both the barge and the train will travel 100 miles to reach New Orleans.

6. How far will the train travel before catching up to the barge?

7. Which shipment will reach New Orleans first? At what time?

8. If both shipments take an hour to unload before heading back to Baton Rouge, what is the earliest time that either one of the companies can begin to load grain to ship in Baton Rouge?

Lesson 5-5

5-5 Enrichment

Cramer's Rule

Cramer's Rule is a method for solving a system of equations. To use Cramer's Rule, set up a matrix to represent the equations. A matrix is a way of organizing data.

Example Solve the following system of equations using Cramer's Rule.
$$2x + 3y = 13$$
$$x + y = 5$$

Step 1: Set up a matrix representing the coefficients of x and y.

$$A = \begin{vmatrix} x & y \\ 2 & 3 \\ 1 & 1 \end{vmatrix}$$

Step 2: Find the determinant of matrix A.

If a matrix $A = \begin{vmatrix} a & b \\ c & d \end{vmatrix}$, then the determinant, $\det(A) = ad - bc$.

$\det(A) = 2(1) - 1(3) = -1$

Step 3: Replace the first column in A with 13 and 5 and find the determinant of the new matrix.

$A_1 = \begin{vmatrix} 13 & 3 \\ 5 & 1 \end{vmatrix}$; $\det(A_1) = 13(1) - 5(3) = -2$

Step 4: To find the value of x in the solution to the system of equations, determine the value of $\frac{\det(A_1)}{\det(A)}$.

$\frac{\det(A_1)}{\det(A)} = \frac{-2}{-1}$ or 2

Step 5: Repeat the process to find the value of y. This time, replace the second column with 13 and 5 and find the determinant.

$A_2 = \begin{vmatrix} 2 & 13 \\ 1 & 5 \end{vmatrix}$; $\det(A_2) = 2(5) - 1(13) = -3$ and $\frac{\det(A_2)}{\det(A)} = \frac{-3}{-1}$ or 3.

So, the solution to the system of equations is (2, 3).

Exercises Use Cramer's Rule to solve each system of equations.

1. $2x + y = 1$
$3x + 5y = 5$

2. $x + y = 4$
$2x - 3y = -2$

3. $x - y = 4$
$3x - 5y = 8$

4. $4x - y = 3$
$x + y = 7$

5. $3x - 2y = 7$
$2x + y = 14$

6. $6x - 5y = 1$
$3x + 2y = 5$

5   Student Recording Sheet

Read each question. Then fill in the correct answer.

1. Ⓐ Ⓑ Ⓒ Ⓓ

2. Ⓕ Ⓖ Ⓗ Ⓘ

3. Record your answer and fill in the bubbles in the grid below. Be sure to use the correct place value.

⓪	⓪	⓪	⓪		⓪	⓪	⓪
①	①	①	①		①	①	①
②	②	②	②		②	②	②
③	③	③	③		③	③	③
④	④	④	④		④	④	④
⑤	⑤	⑤	⑤		⑤	⑤	⑤
⑥	⑥	⑥	⑥		⑥	⑥	⑥
⑦	⑦	⑦	⑦		⑦	⑦	⑦
⑧	⑧	⑧	⑧		⑧	⑧	⑧
⑨	⑨	⑨	⑨		⑨	⑨	⑨

4. Ⓐ Ⓑ Ⓒ Ⓓ

5. Ⓕ Ⓖ Ⓗ Ⓘ

6. Ⓐ Ⓑ Ⓒ Ⓓ

7. Ⓕ Ⓖ Ⓗ Ⓘ

8. Record your answer and fill in the bubbles in the grid below. Be sure to use the correct place value.

⓪	⓪	⓪	⓪		⓪	⓪	⓪
①	①	①	①		①	①	①
②	②	②	②		②	②	②
③	③	③	③		③	③	③
④	④	④	④		④	④	④
⑤	⑤	⑤	⑤		⑤	⑤	⑤
⑥	⑥	⑥	⑥		⑥	⑥	⑥
⑦	⑦	⑦	⑦		⑦	⑦	⑦
⑧	⑧	⑧	⑧		⑧	⑧	⑧
⑨	⑨	⑨	⑨		⑨	⑨	⑨

9. Ⓐ Ⓑ Ⓒ Ⓓ

Pre-AP

Record your answers for Question 10 on the back of this paper.

Assessment

5 Rubric for Scoring Pre-AP

General Scoring Guidelines

- If a student gives only a correct numerical answer to a problem but does not show how he or she arrived at the answer, the student will be awarded only 1 credit. All extended-response questions require the student to show work.
- A fully correct answer for a multiple-part question requires correct responses for all parts of the question. For example, if a question has three parts, the correct response to one or two parts of the question that required work to be shown is *not* considered a fully correct response.
- Students who use trial and error to solve a problem must show their method. Merely showing that the answer checks or is correct is not considered a complete response for full credit.

Exercise 10 Rubric

Score	Specific Criteria
4	The equations written in part a correctly represent the information provided. They show that $7.5a + 4.5c = 3675$ and $a + c = 650$. In parts b, the system of equations is solved correctly to show that $a = 250$ and $c = 400$. These values are determined by first solving one equation in terms of a or c and then replacing that value into the other equation in place of the variable that the equation represents.
3	A generally correct solution, but may contain minor flaws in reasoning or computation.
2	A partially correct interpretation and/or solution to the problem.
1	A correct solution with no evidence or explanation.
0	An incorrect solution indicating no mathematical understanding of the concept or task, or no solution is given.

5 **Chapter 5 Quiz 1**
(Lessons 5-1 and 5-2)

Assessment

Graph each system of equations. Then determine whether the system has *no* solution, *one* solution, or *infinitely many* solutions. If the system has one solution, name it.

1. $y = \frac{3}{2}x$

   $y = -x + 5$

2. $x - 2y = -2$

   $x - 2y = 3$

1.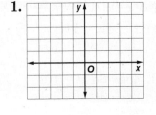

2.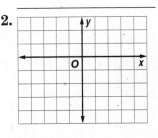

_____

For Questions 3 and 4, use substitution to solve each system of equations. If the system does not have exactly one solution, state whether it has *no* solutions or *infinitely many* solutions.

3. $3x - 2y = -7$

   $y = x + 4$

4. $-6x - 2y = -20$

   $y = -3x + 10$

3. _____

4. _____

5. In order for José and Marty to compete against each other during the wrestling season next year they need to be in the same weight category. José weighs 180 pounds and plans to gain 2 pounds per week. Marty weighs 249 pounds and plans to lose 1 pound per week. In how many weeks will they weigh the same?

5. _____

----

5 **Chapter 5 Quiz 2**
(Lesson 5-3)

For Questions 1–4, use elimination to solve each system of equations.

1. $x + y = 4$

   $x - y = 7$

2. $-2x + y = 5$

   $2x + 3y = 3$

1. _____

2. _____

3. _____

3. $5r - 3s = 17$

   $2r - 3s = 9$

4. $3x = 2 - 7y$

   $-4x = 30 - 7y$

4. _____

5. If $x - 2y = 7$ and $3x - 2y = 1$, what is the value of y?

5. _____

5 Chapter 5 Quiz 3

(Lesson 5-4)

Use elimination to solve each system of equations.

1. $x - 4y = 11$
   $5x - 7y = -10$

2. $2r + 3s = 9$
   $3r + 2s = 12$

3. $4c + 6d = -10$
   $8c - 3d = -5$

4. $2x + 3y = 1$
   $5x - 4y = 14$

5. If $5x - 3y = 7$ and $-3x - 5y = 23$, what is the value of x?
   A. $(-1, -4)$ **B.** $(-4, -1)$ **C.** -4 **D.** -1

1. _____
2. _____
3. _____
4. _____
5. _____

---

5 Chapter 5 Quiz 4

(Lesson 5-5)

Determine the best method to solve each system of equations. Then solve the system.

1. $x = 2y + 1$
   $3x + y = 17$

2. $7x + 5y = 29$
   $21x - 25y = -33$

3. $4x + 2y = 12$
   $-4x + 5y = -5$

4. $x + 3y = -14$
   $x + 2y = -10$

5. You buy 6 videos on sale. The videos are on sale for $8 and $10. You spend $52. How many $8 videos did you buy?

1. _____
2. _____
3. _____
4. _____
5. _____

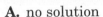

5 Chapter 5 Mid-Chapter Test

SCORE _____

(Lessons 5-1 through 5-3)

Part I *Write the letter for the correct answer in the blank at the right of each question.*

Use the graph for Questions 1–3.

For Questions 1 and 2, determine how many solutions exist for each system of equations.

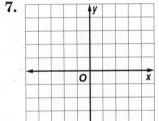

A. no solution

B. one solution

C. infinitely many solutions

D. cannot be determined

1. $x + y = 3$
   $x - y = 3$

2. $x - 3y = -2$
   $y = \frac{1}{3}x + \frac{2}{3}$

1. _____

2. _____

3. The solution to which system of equations has a positive y value?

F. $x + y = 3$
   $x - 3y = -2$

G. $x + y = 3$
   $x + y = -2$

H. $x - 3y = -2$
   $x + y = -2$

J. $x + y = 3$
   $x - y = 3$

3. _____

4. If $y = 5x - 3$ and $3x - y = -1$, what is the value of y?

A. 2   **B.** -1 **C.** 7   **D.** -8

4. _____

5. Use elimination to solve the system of equations for y.

   $x - 5y = -6$
   $x + 2y = 8$

F. $-\frac{2}{3}$ **G.** 2   **H.** 4   **J.** $4\frac{2}{3}$

5. _____

6. How many solutions does the system $2y = 10x - 14$ and $5x - y = 7$ have?

A. one   **B.** two   **C.** none   **D.** infinitely many

6. _____

Part II

7. Graph the system of equations. Then determine whether it has *no* solution, *one* solution, or *infinitely many* solutions. If the system has one solution name it.

   $x - 3y = -3$
   $x + 3y = 9$

7.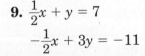

8. Use substitution to solve the system of equations.

   $4x + y = 0$
   $2y + x = -7$

_____

For Questions 9–11, use elimination to solve each system of equations.

9. $\frac{1}{2}x + y = 7$

   $-\frac{1}{2}x + 3y = -11$

10. $2x - 7y = 20$
    $3x + 7y = -5$

8. _____

9. _____

11. $9x + 2y = -17$
    $-11x + 2y = 3$

10. _____

11. _____

12. At the end of the 2000 WNBA regular season, the Houston Comets had 22 more victories than losses. The number of victories they had was three less than six times the number of losses. How many regular season games did the Houston Comets play during the 2000 WNBA season?

12. _____

5 Chapter 5 Vocabulary Test

consistent	elimination	independent	system of equations
dependent	inconsistent	substitution	

Choose from the terms above to complete each sentence.

1. Two equations, such as $y = 3x - 6$ and $y = 12 + 4x$, together are called a ___?___.

   1. _____

2. If the graphs of the equations of a system intersect or coincide, the system of equations is ___?___.

   2. _____

3. If the graphs of the equations of a system are parallel, the system is ___?___.

   3. _____

4. If a system of equations has an infinite number of solutions, the system is ___?___.

   4. _____

5. Sometimes adding two equations of a system will give an equation with only one variable. This is helpful when you are solving the system by ___?___.

   5. _____

Define the terms in your own words.

6. substitiution

   6.

   _____

7. independent

   7.

   _____

5 Chapter 5 Test, Form 1

Write the letter for the correct answer in the blank at the right of each question.

Use the graph for Questions 1–4.

1. The ordered pair (3, 2) is the solution of which system of equations?

   A. $y = -\frac{1}{3}x + 3$ **B.** $y = -\frac{1}{3}x + 3$

   $\quad\ y = -3x + 2$ $\quad\ y = 2x$

   C. $y = -\frac{1}{3}x + 3$ **D.** $y = -3x + 2$

   $\quad\ y = 2x - 4$ $\quad\ y = 2x - 4$

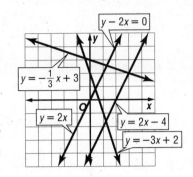

1. _____

For Questions 2–4, find how many solutions exist for each system of equations.

   F. no solution   **H.** one solution

   G. infinitely many solutions   **J.** cannot be determined

2. $y = 2x$
   $y = 2x - 4$

3. $y = 2x$
   $y - 2x = 0$

4. $y = -3x + 2$
   $y = 2x$

2. _____

3. _____

4. _____

5. When solving the system of equations, which expression could be substituted for r in the second equation?

   $r = 4 - s$
   $3r + 2s = 15$

   A. $4 - s$ **B.** $4 - r$ **C.** $s - 4$ **D.** $\frac{4}{s}$

5. _____

6. If $x = 2$ and $3x + y = 5$, what is the value of y?

   F. 0   **G.** -1 **H.** 11   **J.** 10

6. _____

7. Use substitution to solve the system of equations.

   $n = 3m - 11$
   $2m + 3n = 0$

   A. $(-2, 3)$ **B.** $(-3, 2)$ **C.** $(3, -2)$ **D.** $(2, -3)$

7. _____

8. Use elimination to solve the system of equations.

   $x - y = 5$
   $x + y = 3$

   F. $(4, 1)$ **G.** $(4, -1)$ **H.** $(-4, 1)$ **J.** $(-4, -1)$

8. _____

9. Use elimination to solve the system of equations.

   $x + 6y = 10$
   $x + 5y = 9$

   A. $(1, 4)$ **B.** $(4, 1)$ **C.** $(-1, -4)$ **D.** $(-4, -1)$

9. _____

10. Use elimination to find the value of x in the solution for the system of equations.

    $2x + 2y = 10$
    $2x - 3y = 5$

    F. 1   **G.** 10   **H.** 4   **J.** -2

10. _____

11. To eliminate the variable y in the system of equations, multiply the second equation by which number?

    $6x + 4y = 22$
    $2x - y = 1$

    A. 3   **B.** 9   **C.** 22   **D.** 4

11. _____

5 Chapter 5 Test, Form 1 (continued)

12. Use elimination to solve the system of equations.

$2x + 5y = 7$
$3x + 6y = 3$

F. $(-9, 5)$ **G.** $(5, -9)$ **H.** $(-1, 1)$ **J.** $(1, -1)$

12. _____

For Questions 13–15, determine the best method to solve the system of equations.

A. substitution
B. elimination using addition
C. elimination using subtraction
D. elimination using multiplication

13. $5x - 2y = 4$
$2x + 2y = 8$

13. _____

14. $y = 3x + 12$
$2x + y = 16$

14. _____

15. $2x - 4y = 26$
$3x + 2y = 15$

15. _____

16. The length of a rectangle is three times the width. The sum of the length and the width is 24 inches. What is the length of the rectangle?

F. 3 inches **G.** 6 inches **H.** 9 inches **J.** 18 inches

16. _____

17. An airport shuttle company owns sedans that have a maximum capacity of 3 passengers and vans that have a maximum capacity of 8 passengers. Their 12 vehicles have a combined maximum capacity of 61 passengers. How many vans does the company own?

A. 5 **B.** 8 **C.** 12 **D.** 7

17. _____

18. Find the two numbers whose sum is 26 and whose difference is 12.

F. 26 and 12 **G.** 19 and 7 **H.** 14 and 12 **J.** 31 and 19

18. _____

19. Yancy wrote two novels that together contain 580 pages. His longer novel has 160 pages more than his shorter novel. How many pages are contained in Yancy's shorter novel?

A. 290 **B.** 370 **C.** 210 **D.** 130

19. _____

20. Amir has $100 and is saving $5 per week to buy a new DVD player. Pete has $80 and is saving $7 per week to buy the same DVD player. Which system of equations can be used to find w, the number of weeks it would take for them to have m, the money needed to buy the DVD player?

F. $5 + 100w = m$
$80 + 7w = m$

H. $100 + 5w = m$
$7 + 8w = m$

G. $100 + m = 5w$
$80 + m = 7w$

J. $100 + 5w = m$
$80 + 7w = m$

20. _____

Bonus Determine the best method to solve the system of equations. Then solve the system.

$x - 3y = 0$
$2x - 7y = 0$

B: _____

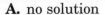

Chapter 5 Test, Form 2A

Write the letter for the correct answer in the blank at the right of each question.

Use the graph for Questions 1–4.

For Questions 1 and 2, determine how many solutions exist for each system of equations.

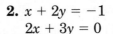

  A. no solution

  B. one solution

  C. infinitely many solutions

  D. cannot be determined

1. $y = 3x + 3$
   $3x - y = 2$

2. $x + 2y = -1$
   $2x + 3y = 0$

1. _____

2. _____

3. The solution to which system of equations has an x value of 3?

  F. $x + 2y = -1$ **G.** $3x - y = 2$ **H.** $y = 3x + 3$ **J.** $2x + 3y = 0$
     $y = 3x + 3$ $x + 2y = -1$ $2x + 3y = 0$ $x + 2y = -1$

3. _____

4. The solution to which system of equations has a y value of 0?

  A. $x + 2y = -1$ **B.** $3x - y = 2$ **C.** $y = 3x + 3$ **D.** $2x + 3y = 0$
     $y = 3x + 3$ $x + 2y = -1$ $2x + 3y = 0$ $x + 2y = -1$

4. _____

5. When solving the system of equations, which expression could be substituted for x in the second equation?

                                $x + 2y = 15$
                                  $5x + y = 21$

  F. $15 - 2y$ **G.** $21 - 5x$ **H.** $\dfrac{15 - x}{2}$ **J.** $\dfrac{21 - y}{5}$

5. _____

6. If $x = 2y + 3$ and $4x - 5y = 9$, what is the value of y?

  A. 2   **B.** 1   **C.** -1 **D.** -2

6. _____

7. Use elimination to solve the system $x + 7y = 16$ and $3x - 7y = 4$ for x.

  F. 3   **G.** 4   **H.** 5   **J.** -6

7. _____

8. Use elimination to solve the system $x - 5y = 20$ and $x + 3y = -4$ for x.

  A. 5   **B.** -3 **C.** 10   **D.** -40

8. _____

9. Use elimination to solve the system $8x - 7y = 5$ and $3x - 5y = 9$ for y.

  F. -2 **G.** 8   **H.** -3 **J.** -1

9. _____

10. Use elimination to solve the system $4x + 6y = 10$ and $2x + 5y = 1$ for x.

  A. 11   **B.** $5\dfrac{1}{2}$ **C.** -2 **D.** $-\dfrac{1}{2}$

10. _____

11. The substitution method should be used to solve which system of equations?

  F. $4x + 3y = 6$ **G.** $2x + 5y = 1$ **H.** $6x + 2y = 1$ **J.** $y = 3x + 1$
     $5x - 3y = 2$ $2x - 3y = 4$ $3x + 4y = 7$ $2x + 4y = 5$

11. _____

12. The elimination method using multiplication should be used to solve which system of equations?

    A. $x = 7y + 1$ **B.** $3x + 2y = 1$ **C.** $x - y = 16$ **D.** $3x + y = -15$ **12.** _____
    $\quad\;\; 2x - y = 8$ $4x - 3y = 12$ $2x + y = 9$ $3x + 5y = 10$

13. The elimination method using addition should be used to solve which system of equations?

    F. $2x - 5y = -7$ **G.** $x - y = 8$ **H.** $2x - 3y = 5$ **J.** $y = x + 2$ **13.** _____
    $\quad\; -3x + 6y = 10$ $6x + 2y = -7$ $4x + 3y = 1$ $2x - y = 8$

14. Use substitution to solve the system $x + 2y = 1$ and $2x + 5y = 3$.

    A. $(-1, 1)$ **B.** $(1, -1)$ **C.** $(-5, 3)$ **D.** $(-1, -1)$ **14.** _____

For Questions 15 and 16, solve the system and find values of y.

15. $3x - 5y = -35$ **F.** 4   **G.** $\frac{4}{5}$ **H.** -4 **J.** $-\frac{4}{5}$ **15.** _____
    $2x - 5y = -30$

16. $3x + 4y = -30$ **A.** -6 **B.** 6   **C.** -12 **D.** 12   **16.** _____
    $2x - 5y = 72$

17. Two times one number added to three times a second number is 21. Five times the first number added to three times the second number is 30. What are the numbers?

    F. 21 and 30   **G.** 3 and 2   **H.** 6 and 1   **J.** 3 and 5   **17.** _____

18. Coffee Cafe makes 90 pounds of coffee that costs $6 per pound. The types of coffee used to make this mixture cost $7 per pound and $4 per pound. How many pounds of the $7-per-pound coffee should be used in this mixture?

    A. 30 lb   **B.** 40 lb   **C.** 50 lb   **D.** 60 lb   **18.** _____

19. In 1999, there were 59,549 physicians specializing in Pediatrics in the United States and its possessions. The number of male physicians minus the number of female physicians in this category is 2551. How many female physicians were there that specialized in Pediatrics in the United States?

    F. 29,774   **G.** 28,499   **H.** 31,050   **J.** 27,223   **19.** _____

20. Your teacher is giving a test that has 5 more four-point questions than six-point questions. The test is worth 120 points. Which system represents this information?

    A. $x + 5 = y$ **B.** $x + y = 5$ **C.** $x - y = 5$ **D.** $x - y = 5$ **20.** _____
    $\quad\; 4x + 6y = 120$ $6x + 4y = 120$ $6x + 4y = 120$ $4x + 6y = 120$

Bonus Where on the graph of $2x - 6y = 7$ is the x-coordinate   **B:**
twice the y-coordinate?

_____

5 Chapter 5 Test, Form 2B

SCORE _____

Write the letter for the correct answer in the blank at the right of each question.

Use the graph for Questions 1–4.

For Questions 1 and 2, determine how many solutions exist for each system of equations.

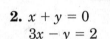

A. no solution

B. one solution

C. infinitely many solutions

D. cannot be determined

1. $3x - 3y = -6$
   $y = x + 2$

2. $x + y = 0$
   $3x - y = 2$

1. _____

2. _____

3. The solution to which system of equations has an x value of -1?

   F. $x + y = 0$
       $3x - y = 2$

   G. $3x - y = 2$
       $y = -x - 2$

   H. $x + y = 0$
       $3x - 3y = -6$

   J. $y = -x - 2$
       $x + y = 0$

   3. _____

4. The solution to which system of equations has a y value of -2?

   A. $x + y = 0$
       $3x - y = 2$

   B. $3x - y = 2$
       $y = -x - 2$

   C. $x + y = 0$
       $3x - 3y = -6$

   D. $y = -x - 2$
       $x + y = 0$

   4. _____

5. When solving the system of equations, which expression could be substituted for y in the second equation?

   $3x + y = 14$
   $x + 4y = 3$

   F. $3 - 4y$

   G. $\dfrac{3 - x}{4}$

   H. $\dfrac{14 - y}{3}$

   J. $14 - 3x$

   5. _____

6. If $x = 5y - 1$ and $2x + 5y = -32$, what is the value of y?

   A. -2 **B.** 2 **C.** 1 **D.** -1

   6. _____

7. Use elimination to solve the system $3x + 5y = 16$ and $8x - 5y = 28$ for x.

   F. -6 **G.** 5 **H.** 4 **J.** $\dfrac{4}{5}$

   7. _____

8. Use elimination to solve the system $x - 4y = 1$ and $x + 2y = 19$ for x.

   A. -11 **B.** 3 **C.** 25 **D.** 13

   8. _____

9. Use elimination to solve the system $4x + 7y = -14$ and $8x + 5y = 8$ for x.

   F. $3\dfrac{1}{2}$ **G.** $-1\dfrac{1}{2}$ **H.** 8 **J.** -4

   9. _____

10. Use elimination to solve the system $5x + 4y = -10$ and $3x + 6y = -6$ for y.

    A. -2 **B.** -5 **C.** 0 **D.** 2

    10. _____

11. The substitution method should be used to solve which system of equations?

    F. $5x - 7y = 16$
        $2x - 7y = 12$

    G. $4x + 3y = -5$
        $6x - 3y = 2$

    H. $x = 3y + 1$
        $2x + y = 7$

    J. $2x + 6y = 3$
        $3x + 2y = -1$

    11. _____

12. The elimination method using addition should be used to solve which system of equations?

A. $y = -4x + 1$ **B.** $x + 2y = -4$ **C.** $5x + y = -6$ **D.** $x - 4y = -9$ 12. _____
    $x - 2y = 7$ $3x - 2y = -1$ $5x - 2y = 3$ $-8x - y = 1$

13. The elimination method using multiplication should be used to solve which system of equations?

F. $y = -2x + 10$ **G.** $4x + 3y = -2$ **H.** $3x - y = 6$ **J.** $4x - 2y = 8$ 13. _____
    $-2x + 3y = 6$ $2x + 6y = 8$ $2x + y = 8$ $3x - 2y = -6$

14. Use substitution to solve the system $x - 2y = 1$ and $6x - 5y = 20$.

A. $(2, 5)$ **B.** $(-5, -2)$ **C.** $(5, 2)$ **D.** $(-2, -5)$ 14. _____

For Questions 15 and 16, solve the system and find the value of *y*.

15. $2x + 3y = 1$ **F.** $-8\frac{3}{7}$ **G.** $8\frac{3}{7}$ **H.** -3 **J.** 3 15. _____
   $5x - 4y = -32$

16. $6x + 3y = 12$ **A.** -20 **B.** $-1\frac{9}{11}$ **C.** 20 **D.** $1\frac{9}{11}$ 16. _____
   $5x + 3y = 0$

17. Five times one number minus two times a second number is 11. Three times the first number minus two times the second number is 1. What are the numbers?

F. 5 and 7   **G.** 2 and 5   **H.** 11 and 1   **J.** 4 and -6 17. _____

18. Colortime Bakers wants to make 30 pounds of a berry mix that costs $3 per pound to use in their pancake mix. They are using blueberries that cost $2 per pound and blackberries that cost $3.50 per pound. How many pounds of blackberries should be used in this mixture?

A. 15 lb   **B.** 20 lb   **C.** 10 lb   **D.** 30 lb   18. _____

19. In 1999, there were 69,063 physicians specializing in Family Practice in the United States and its possessions. The number of male physicians minus the number of female physicians in this category is 31,289. How many female physicians were there that specialized in Family Practice in the United States?

F. 50,176   **G.** 34,531   **H.** 3243   **J.** 18,887   19. _____

20. Your teacher is giving a test that has 12 more three-point questions than five-point questions. The test is worth 100 points. Which system represents this information?

A. $x + y = 12$ **B.** $x + y = 12$ **C.** $x - y = 12$ **D.** $x - y = 12$ 20. _____
    $3x + 5y = 100$ $5x + 3y = 100$ $3x + 5y = 100$ $5x + 3y = 100$

Bonus Manuel is 8 years older than his sister. Three years ago he was 3 times older than his sister. How old is each now? **B:** _____

5 **Chapter 5 Test, Form 2C**

Use the graph at the right to determine whether each system has *no* **solution,** *one* **solution, or** *infinitely many* **solutions.**

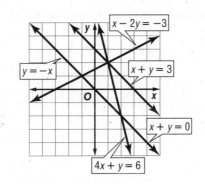

1. $y = -x$
   $x + y = 3$

2. $x - 2y = -3$
   $4x + y = 6$

Graph each system of equations. Then determine whether the system has *no* **solution,** *one* **solution, or** *infinitely many* **solutions. If the system has one solution, name it.**

3. $y = -x + 4$
   $y = x - 4$

4. $2x - y = -3$
   $6x - 3y = -9$

5. $x + y = -2$
   $x + y = 3$

Use substitution to solve each system of equations. If the system does not have exactly one solution, state whether it has *no* **solution or** *infinitely many* **solutions.**

6. $y = 3x$
   $x + y = 4$

7. $5x - y = 10$
   $7x - 2y = 11$

8. $x - 6y = 4$
   $3x - 18y = 4$

9. $x - 5y = 10$
   $2x - 10y = 20$

Use elimination to solve each system of equations.

10. $x + 4y = -8$
    $x - 4y = -8$

11. $2x + 5y = 3$
    $-x + 3y = -7$

12. $2x - 5y = -16$
    $-2x + 3y = 12$

13. $2x + 5y = 9$
    $2x + y = 13$

14. $2x - 3y = 1$
    $5x + 4y = 14$

15. $x - 3y = 10$
    $x + 2y = 15$

1. _____

2. _____

3.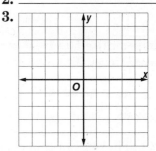

4.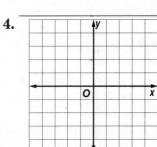

5.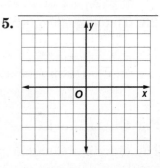

_____

6. _____

7. _____

8. _____

9. _____

10. _____

11. _____

12. _____

13. _____

14. _____

15. _____

5 Chapter 5 Test, Form 2C *(continued)*

Determine the best method to solve each system of equations. Then solve the system.

16. $x = 2y - 1$
    $3x + y = 11$

17. $5x - y = 17$
    $3x - y = 13$

Determine the best method to solve each system of equations. Then solve the system.

18. $8x + 3y = 15$
    $5x - 2y = -10$

19. $2x - 4y = 16$
    $4x + 4y = -4$

20. The sum of two numbers is 17 and their difference is 29. What are the two numbers?

21. Adult tickets for the school musical sold for $3.50 and student tickets sold for $2.50. Three hundred twenty-one tickets were sold altogether for $937.50. How many of each kind of ticket were sold?

22. Ayana has $2.35 in nickels and dimes. If she has 33 coins in all, find the number of nickels and dimes.

23. The largest county in the state of New York is 1769 square miles larger than the smallest county in the same state. The size of the largest county is 64 times the size of the smallest county plus five square miles. How large is the smallest county in the state of New York?

For Questions 24 and 25, use the following information.

The Martinez Company manufactures two types of industrial fans, standard and economy. These items are built using machines and manual labor. The table gives the time requirements at each type of workstation for each type of fan.

	Hours per Standard Fan	Hours per Economy Fan	Total Hours Each Week
Machines	3	3	1500
Manual Labor	2	1	800

24. Define variables and formulate a system of linear equations from this situation.

25. How many standard fans can be made in a week?

Bonus Mavis is 5 years older than her brother. Five years ago she was 2 times older than her brother. How old is each now?

16. _____

17. _____

18. _____

19. _____

20. _____

21. _____

22. _____

23. _____

24. _____

25. _____

B: _____

5 **Chapter 5 Test, Form 2D**

Use the graph at the right to determine whether each system has *no* solution, *one* solution, or *infinitely many* solutions.

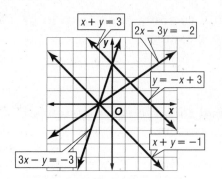

1. $x + y = 3$
   $y = -x + 3$

2. $3x - y = -3$
   $2x - 3y = -2$

Graph each system of equations. Then determine whether the system has *no* solution, *one* solution, or *infinitely many* solutions. If the system has one solution, name it.

3. $y = -x + 3$
   $y = x - 3$

4. $2x - y = 5$
   $4x - 2y = 10$

5. $x + y = 0$
   $x + y = 2$

Use substitution to solve each system of equations. If the system does not have exactly one solution, state whether it has *no* solution or *infinitely many* solutions.

6. $y = 2x$
   $2x + y = 8$

7. $2x - y = 3$
   $5x + 7y = 17$

8. $x - 5y = 2$
   $4x - 20y = 8$

9. $x + 3y = -2$
   $4x + 12y = 7$

Use elimination to solve each system of equations.

10. $2x + 3y = 19$
    $2x - 3y = 1$

11. $6x + 4y = 20$
    $4x - 2y = 4$

12. $2x + 2y = 6$
    $3x - 2y = -11$

13. $7x + 3y = 1$
    $9x + 3y = -3$

14. $2x - 3y = 23$
    $3x + 5y = 6$

15. $x + 3y = 0$
    $x - 5y = 16$

1. _____

2. _____

3.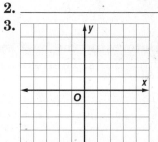

4.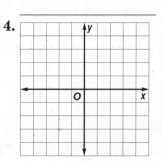

5.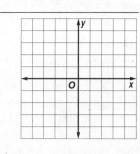

   _____

6. _____

7. _____

8. _____

9. _____

10. _____

11. _____

12. _____

13. _____

14. _____

15. _____

5 Chapter 5 Test, Form 2D (continued)

Determine the best method to solve each system of equations. Then solve the system.

16. $y = 3x + 1$
$x - 2y = 8$

17. $5x - 15y = -20$
$5x - 4y = -9$

16. _____

17. _____

Determine the best method to solve each system of equations. Then solve the system.

18. $-3x + 9y = 48$
$4x - 2y = -14$

19. $4x - 5y = 2$
$-7x + 5y = -11$

18. _____

19. _____

20. The sum of two numbers is 16 and their difference is 20. What are the two numbers?

20. _____

21. Kyle just started a new job that pays $7 per hour. He had been making $5 per hour at his old job. Kyle worked a total of 54 hours last month and made $338 before deductions. How many hours did he work at his new job?

21. _____

22. So far this basketball season, all of Nikki's points have come from two-point and three-point field goals. She has scored a total of 43 points. The number of three-point field goals she has made is one more than twice as many two-point field goals. How many of each type of field goal has Nikki made?

22. _____

23. The largest county in the state of Texas is 6064 square miles larger than the smallest county in the same state. The size of the largest county is 48 times the size of the smallest county plus one square mile. How large is the smallest county in the state of Texas?

23. _____

For Questions 24 and 25, use the following information.

The Tadashi Corporation manufactures a large speaker and a small speaker for phone headsets. The speakers are used on the Tadashi 200 and the Tadashi 500 phone systems. The table gives the speaker requirement for each phone system.

	Speakers on Tadashi 200	Speakers on Tadashi 500	Total Available Speakers Each Week
Large Speaker	2	3	900
Small Speaker	2	4	1000

24. Define variables and formulate a system of linear equations from this situation.

24. _____

25. How many Tadashi 200 phone systems can be made in a week?

25. _____

Bonus Find the point on the graph of $3x - 4y = 9$ where the y-coordinate is 3 times the x-coordinate.

B: _____

5 **Chapter 5 Test, Form 3**

SCORE _____

Graph each system of equations. Determine whether the system has *no* solution, *one* solution, or *infinitely many* solutions. If the system has one solution, name it.

1. $\frac{1}{3}y = x$

$y + x + 4 = 0$

2. $x + 3y = 3$

$3y = -x + 9$

3. $\frac{1}{2} + \frac{1}{2}y = x$

$2x - y = 1$

1.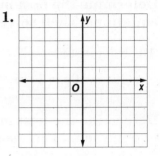

2.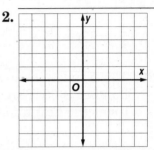

3.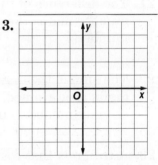

Use substitution to solve each system of equations. If the system does not have exactly one solution, state whether it has *no* solution or *infinitely many* solutions.

4. $y = 2x - 7$

$3x - 4y = 8$

5. $4y - 3x = 5$

$\frac{3}{4}x = y - 4$

6. $\frac{1}{2}x - 5y = 19$

$x - 2y = -10$

7. $0.5x + 3.5y = 1$

$x = 2 - 7y$

8. $x - 2y = -3$

$y = 3x - 1$

9. $y = -x + 3$

$x + y = -1$

Use elimination to solve each system of equations.

10. $6x - 7y = 21$

$3x + 7y = 6$

11. $0.2x + 0.5y = 0.7$

$-0.2x - 0.6y = -1.4$

12. $2x + \frac{2}{3}y = -8$

$\frac{1}{2}x - \frac{1}{3}y = 1$

13. $\frac{1}{2}x + \frac{2}{5}y = -10$

$3x + 6y = -6$

14. $0.4x - 0.1y = 1$

$0.5x - 0.1y = 1.6$

15. $\frac{3}{4}x + \frac{1}{2}y = 1\frac{1}{2}$

$\frac{3}{4}x + y = 4\frac{1}{2}$

4. _____

5. _____

6. _____

7. _____

8. _____

9. _____

10. _____

11. _____

12. _____

13. _____

14. _____

15. _____

Determine the best method to solve each system of equations. Then solve the system.

16. $x + y = 147$

$25x + 10y = 2415$

17. $7y = 2\frac{1}{2} - 2x$

$5x = 3y - 4$

16. _____

17. _____

Determine the best method to solve each system of equations. Then solve the system.

18. $\frac{1}{2}x + \frac{3}{4}y = -2$

$\frac{1}{4}x - \frac{3}{4}y = \frac{7}{2}$

19. $0.5x + 4.1y = 2.8$

$0.5x - 2.1y = -15.8$

18. _____

19. _____

20. Three times one number added to five times a second number is 68. Three times the second number minus four times the first number is 6. What are the two numbers?

20. _____

21. The difference of two numbers is 5. Five times the lesser number minus the greater number is 9. What are the two numbers?

21. _____

22. The sum of the digits of a 2-digit number is 13. If the digits are reversed, the new number is 9 more than the original number. Find the original number.

22. _____

23. A trail mix that costs $2.45 per pound is mixed with a trail mix that costs $2.30 per pound. How much of each type of trail mix must be used to have 30 pounds of a trail mix that costs $2.35 per pound?

23. _____

24. A boat travels 60 miles downstream in the same time it takes to go 36 miles upstream. The speed of the boat in still water is 15 mph greater than the speed of the current. Find the speed of the current.

24. _____

25. Mrs. Lewis needs to buy two types of grain, oats and barley, to mix as a feed supplement for her cattle. She has $4275 to spend on grain, and wants the mixture to be 3 parts oats and 2 parts barley. She can buy oats for $1.10 per bushel and barley for $2.10 per bushel. Mrs. Lewis needs 7,000 bushels of grain. How many bushels of barley should she buy?

25. _____

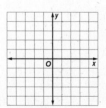

Bonus Find the area of the polygon formed by the system of equations $y = 0$, $y = 2x + 4$ and $-3y - 4x = -12$. Use the graph on the right.

B: _____

5 **Chapter 5 Extended-Response Test**

Demonstrate your knowledge by giving a clear, concise solution to each problem. Be sure to include all relevant drawings and justify your answers. You may show your solution in more than one way or investigate beyond the requirements of the problem.

1. Ruth invests $10,000 in two accounts. One account has an annual interest rate of 7%, and the other account has an annual interest rate of 5%. Let I represent the total interest earned in one year. Then Ruth's investments can be modeled by the system of equations $x + y = 10,000$ and $0.07x + 0.05y = I$.

   a. Determine a solution for this system of equations that represents a possible investment, and find the value of I that corresponds to your solution.

   b. Find the solution for the system if $I = 800$. Explain why this solution does not represent a possible investment.

2. A car rental company wants to charge a rate of $\$A$ per day plus $\$B$ per mile to rent a compact car. Their leading competitor charges $15 per day plus $0.25 per mile to rent a compact car.

   a. Explain how the system of equations $y = A + Bx$ and $y = 15 + 0.25x$ compares the total cost of renting a compact car for one day from this company and from their leading competitor.

   b. Describe how the value of A and the value of B affects the comparison of the total cost of any one-day rental from these two companies.

3. A bookstore makes a profit of $2.50 on each book they sell, and $0.75 on each magazine they sell. Each week the store sells x books and y magazines. Let $\$P$ be the weekly profit, and $\$S$ be the weekly sales for the bookstore.

   a. Write a system of equations that models the possible weekly sales and weekly profit for the book store. Then describe possible values for P and S.

   b. Choose a value for P and a value for S, and substitute the values into the system of equations from part **a**. Make a graph of this system of equations, and describe what the graph represents.

59

5 **Standardized Test Practice**

SCORE _____

(Chapters 1-5)

Part 1: Multiple Choice
Instructions: Fill in the appropriate circle for the best answer.

1. Which equation is *not* equivalent to $x - 7 = 12$? (Lesson 2-2)

   A $x - 9 = 14$ **B** $x - 10 = 9$ **C** $x = 19$ **D** $x - 3 = 16$ **1.** Ⓐ Ⓑ Ⓒ Ⓓ

2. Find the value of y so that the line through $(2, 3)$ and $(5, y)$ has a slope of -2. (Lesson 4-1)

   F -3 **G** $\frac{3}{2}$ **H** 9 **J** $\frac{9}{2}$ **2.** Ⓕ Ⓖ Ⓗ Ⓙ

3. Solve $-8x - 15 = -31$. (Lesson 2-4)

   A -2 **B** 6 **C** 2 **D** -6 **3.** Ⓐ Ⓑ Ⓒ Ⓓ

4. If $f(x) = 3(x - 5)$, find $f(4)$. (Lesson 3-2)

   F 7 **G** 27 **H** -3 **J** 3 **4.** Ⓕ Ⓖ Ⓗ Ⓙ

5. Which equation shows the slope-intercept form of the line passing through $(0, 1)$ and $(2, 0)$? (Lesson 4-4)

   A $y = -2x + 1$ **B** $y = \frac{1}{2}x - 1$ **C** $y = 2x - 1$ **D** $y = -\frac{1}{2}x + 1$ **5.** Ⓐ Ⓑ Ⓒ Ⓓ

6. How many solutions exist for the system of equations? (Lesson 5-1)
   $2x - 3y = 14$
   $4x - 6y = 21$

   F no solutions   **H** one solution
   G two solutions   **J** infinitely many solutions   **6.** Ⓕ Ⓖ Ⓗ Ⓙ

7. When solving the following system, which expression could be substituted for y? (Lesson 5-2)
   $5x - 12y = 6$
   $7x + y = 3$

   A $7x - 3$ **B** $-7x + 3$ **C** $5x - 6$ **D** $-5x + 6$ **7.** Ⓐ Ⓑ Ⓒ Ⓓ

8. If $4x + 5y = 6$ and $7x + 5y = 3$, what is the value of y? (Lesson 5-3)

   F -1 **G** 2 **H** 1 **J** -3 **8.** Ⓕ Ⓖ Ⓗ Ⓙ

9. Use elimination to solve the system of equations. (Lesson 5-3)
   $x + 2y = 9$
   $3x - 2y = 3$

   A $(0, 4)$ **B** $(3, 3)$ **C** $(4, -2)$ **D** $(5, 1)$ **9.** Ⓐ Ⓑ Ⓒ Ⓓ

10. Which of the following is an arithmetic sequence? (Lesson 3-4)

   F $1, 3, 6, 10, …$ **H** $34, 35, 38, 43, …$
   G $5, 8, 11, 14, …$ **J** $1, 4, 9, 16, …$ **10.** Ⓕ Ⓖ Ⓗ Ⓙ

5   **Standardized Test Practice**   *(continued)*

11. Determine which is a linear equation. (Lesson 3-3)

    A $\dfrac{1}{x} - y = 7$ **C** $3 = xy$

    B $x^2 - 4 = y$ **D** $x - y = 4$ **11.** Ⓐ Ⓑ Ⓒ Ⓓ

12. Find the discounted price.   Pants: $24 (Lesson 2-7)
Discount: 15%

    F $20.40   **G** $3.60   **H** $20   **J** $9   **12.** Ⓕ Ⓖ Ⓗ Ⓙ

13. Solve $8x - 5 = 23 + 4x$. (Lesson 2-5)

    A 4.5   **B** 7   **C** 23   **D** 5   **13.** Ⓐ Ⓑ Ⓒ Ⓓ

14. Rewrite $5(a - b + c)$ using the Distributive Property. (Lesson 1-5)

    F $5a - b + c$ **H** $5a - 5b + 5c$

    G $5a + 5b + c$ **J** $5a + b + c$ **14.** Ⓕ Ⓖ Ⓗ Ⓙ

15. Write an equation that passes through $(3, 2)$ and has a slope of -2. (Lesson 4-4)

    A $y = 8x - 2$ **C** $y = -2x + 7$

    B $y = -2x + 8$ **D** $y = -2x + 2$ **15.** Ⓐ Ⓑ Ⓒ Ⓓ

16. Find the slope of the line that passes through $(-7, 8)$ and $(-6, 5)$. (Lesson 4-2)

    F -3 **G** $-\dfrac{1}{3}$ **H** 3   **J** -6 **16.** Ⓕ Ⓖ Ⓗ Ⓙ

17. Evaluate the expression if $x = 4$, $y = 3$, and $z = 2$. (Lesson 1-2)
$x^2 + 4y + z$

    A 27   **B** 22   **C** 20   **D** 30   **17.** Ⓐ Ⓑ Ⓒ Ⓓ

Part 2: Griddable

Instructions: Enter your answer by writing each digit of the answer in a column box and then shading in the appropriate circle that corresponds to that entry.

18. What is the slope of a line parallel to the line that passes through $(-3, 1)$ and $(3, 7)$? (Lesson 4-7)

19. If $4x + 7y = -3$ and $3x + 2y = 14$, what is the value of x? (Lesson 5-4)

5 Standardized Test Practice *(continued)*

Part 3: Short Answer

Instructions: Write your answers in the space provided.

20. Solve $\frac{a}{6} - 5 = 12$. (Lesson 4-4)

20. _____

21. If $f(x) = x^2 - 4x$, find $f(-3)$. (Lesson 4-6)

21. _____

22. Solve $y = \frac{1}{4}x - 1$ if the domain is $\{-4, -2, 0, 2, 4\}$. (Lesson 3-3)

22. _____

23. Write the slope-intercept form of an equation of the line that passes through $(0, -4)$ and is parallel to the graph of $4x - y = 7$. (Lesson 4-7)

23. _____

24. Solve $\frac{4}{5}a \le -12$. (Lesson 2-3)

24. _____

25. Solve the proportion $\frac{.6}{x} = \frac{.3}{5}$. (Lesson 2-6)

25. _____

26. Graph the system of equations. Then determine whether the system has *no* solution, *one* solution, or *infinitely many* solutions. (Lesson 5-1)
$$3x - y = 1$$
$$y = 3x + 1$$

26. _____

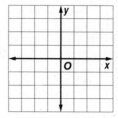

27. The sum of two numbers is 21, and their difference is 7. What are the numbers? (Lesson 5-3)

27. _____

28. Use elimination to solve the system of equations. (Lesson 5-4)
$$2x - 4y = 26$$
$$3x + 2y = 15$$

28. _____

29. Graph the equation $y = x - 4$ (Lesson 3-3)

29.

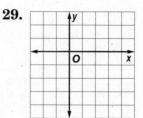

30. Jim's Brakes charges \$25 for parts and \$55 per hour to fix the brakes on a car. Myron's Auto charges \$40 for parts and \$30 per hour to do the same job.

30a. Write a system of equations that could be used to solve this problem. (Lesson 5-2)

30a. _____

30b. What length of job in hours would have the same cost at both shops? (Lesson 5-2)

30b. _____

NAME _____ DATE _____ PERIOD _____

5-4 Enrichment

George Washington Carver and Percy Julian

In 1990, George Washington Carver and Percy Julian became the first African Americans elected to the National Inventors Hall of Fame. Carver (1864–1943) was an agricultural scientist known worldwide for developing hundreds of uses for the peanut and the sweet potato. His work revitalized the economy of the southern United States because it was no longer dependent solely upon cotton. Julian (1898–1975) was a research chemist who became famous for inventing a method of making a synthetic cortisone from soybeans. His discovery has had many medical applications, particularly in the treatment of arthritis.

There are dozens of other African American inventors whose accomplishments are not as well known. Their inventions range from common household items like the ironing board to complex devices that have revolutionized manufacturing. The exercises that follow will help you identify just a few of these inventors and their inventions.

Match the inventors with their inventions by matching each system with its solution. (Not all the solutions will be used.)

1. Sara Boone	$x + y = 2$ $\quad$ **E** $x - y = 10$	**A.** (1, 4)	automatic traffic signal
2. Sarah Goode	$x = 2 - y$ $\quad$ **D** $2y + x = 9$	**B.** (4, −2)	eggbeater
3. Frederick M. Jones	$y = 2x + 6$ $\quad$ **G** $y = -x - 3$	**C.** (−2, 3)	fire extinguisher
4. J. L. Love	$2x + 3y = 8$ $\quad$ **F** $2x - y = -8$	**D.** (−5, 7)	folding cabinet bed
5. T. J. Marshall	$y - 3x = 9$ $\quad$ **C** $2y + x = 4$	**E.** (6, −4)	ironing board
6. Jan Matzeliger	$y + 4 = 2x$ $\quad$ **J** $6x - 3y = 12$	**F.** (−2, 4)	pencil sharpener
7. Garrett A. Morgan	$3x - 2y = -5$ $\quad$ **A** $3y - 4x = 8$	**G.** (−3, 0)	portable X-ray machine
8. Norbert Rillieux	$3x - y = 12$ $\quad$ **I** $y - 3x = 15$	**H.** (2, −3)	player piano
		I. no solution	evaporating pan for refining sugar
		J. infinitely many solutions	lasting (shaping) machine for manufacturing shoes

Chapter 5 $\qquad$ 33 $\qquad$ *Glencoe Algebra 1*

NAME _____ DATE _____ PERIOD _____

5-4 Word Problem Practice

Elimination Using Multiplication

1. SOCCER Suppose a youth soccer field has a perimeter of 320 yards and its length measures 40 yards more than its width. Ms. Hughey asks her players to determine the length and width of their field. She gives them the following system of equations to represent the situation. Use elimination to solve the system to find the length and width of the field.

$$2L + 2W = 320$$
$$L - W = 40$$

width = 60 yd; length = 100 yd

2. SPORTS The Fan Cost Index (FCI) tracks the average costs for attending sporting events, including tickets, drinks, food, parking, programs, and souvenirs. According to the FCI, a family of four would spend a total of $592.30 to attend two Major League Baseball (MLB) games and one National Basketball Association (NBA) game. The family would spend $691.31 to attend one MLB and two NBA games. Write and solve a system of equations to find the family's costs for each kind of game according to the FCI. **NBA: $263.44; MLB: $164.43**

3. ART Mr. Santos, the curator of the children's museum, recently made two purchases of clay and wood for a visiting artist to sculpt. Use the table to find the cost of each product per kilogram.

Clay (kg)	Wood (kg)	Total Cost
5	4	$35.50
3.5	6	$50.45

Clay was $0.70 per kilogram and wood was $8.00 per kilogram.

4. TRAVEL Antonio flies from Houston to Philadelphia, a distance of about 1340 miles. His plane travels with the wind and takes 2 hours and 20 minutes. At the same time, Paul is on a plane from Philadelphia to Houston. Since his plane is heading against the wind, Paul's flight takes 2 hours and 50 minutes. What was the speed of the wind in miles per hour? **about 50.67 mph**

BUSINESS For Exercises 5–7, use the following information.

Suppose you start a business assembling and selling motorized scooters. It costs you $1500 for tools and equipment to get started, and the materials cost $200 for each scooter. Your scooters sell for $300 each.

5. Write and solve a system of equations representing the total costs and revenue of your business. $y = 200x + 1500$ **(cost);** $y = 300x$ **(revenue); solution: (15, 4500)**

6. Describe what the solution means in terms of the situation. **The solution represents the point at which cost equals revenue. This is the break-even point for the business owner.**

7. Give an example of a reasonable number of scooters you could assemble and sell in order to make a profit, and find the profit you would make for that number of scooters. **Sample answer: 20 scooters: It costs $5500 to assemble these scooters, which sell for $6000, leaving a $500 profit.**

Chapter 5 $\qquad$ 32 $\qquad$ *Glencoe Algebra 1*

Answers

Answers (Lesson 5-5)

NAME _____ DATE _____ PERIOD _____

5-5 Study Guide and Intervention

Applying Systems of Linear Equations

DETERMINE THE BEST METHOD You have learned five methods for solving systems of linear equations: graphing, substitution, elimination using addition, elimination using subtraction, and elimination using multiplication. For an exact solution, an algebraic method is best.

Example At a baseball game, Henry bought 3 hotdogs and a bag of chips for $14. Scott bought 2 hotdogs and a bag of chips for $10. The hotdogs and chips were all the same price, so the following system of equations can be used to represent the situation. Determine the best method to solving the system of equations. Then solve the system.

$3x + y = 14$
$2x + y = 10$

- Since neither the coefficients of x nor the coefficients of y are additive inverses, you cannot use elimination using addition.
- Since the coefficient of y in both equations is 1, you can use elimination using subtraction. You could also use the substitution method or elimination using multiplication.

The following solution uses elimination by subtraction to solve this system.

$$\begin{array}{rl} 3x + y = & 14 \\ (-)\, 2x + (-)\, y = & (-)10 \end{array}$$ Write the equations in column form and subtract.

$\qquad x \qquad = \quad 4$ The variable y is eliminated.
$3(4) + \quad y = \quad 14$ Substitute the value for x back into the first equation.
$\qquad y = \quad 2$ Solve for y.

This means that hot dogs cost $4 each and a bag of chips costs $2.

Exercises

Determine the best method to solve each system of equations. Then solve the system.

1. $5x + 3y = 16$
   $3x - 5y = -4$
   elimination (×); (2, 2)

2. $3x - 5y = 7$
   $2x + 5y = 13$
   elimination (+); (4, 1)

3. $y + 3x = 24$
   $5x - y = 24$
   elimination (+); (4, 12)

4. $-11x - 10y = 17$
   $5x - 7y = 50$
   elimination (×); (3, −5)

Chapter 5   35   Glencoe Algebra 1

NAME _____ DATE _____ PERIOD _____

5-5 Lesson Reading Guide

Applying Systems of Linear Equations

Get Ready For the Lesson

Do the activity at the beginning of the lesson in your textbook.

a. Write an equation to describe the total length of both tours. $x + y = 3.25$

b. Write an equation to describe the relationship between the length of the Crystal Palace tour and then Horseshoe Lake tour. $x = 2y$

c. Combine both equations into a system of equations. Use any method to solve for the lengths of the tours. $x = 2\frac{1}{6}; y = 1\frac{1}{12}$

Read the Lesson
Complete the following chart.

Method	The Best Time to Use
Graphing	to estimate the solution, since graphing usually does not give an exact solution
Substitution	if one of the variables in either equation has a coefficient of 1 or −1
Elimination Using Addition	if one of the variables has opposite coefficients in the two equations
Elimination Using Subtraction	if one of the variables has the same coefficient in the two equations
Elimination Using Multiplication	if none of the coefficients are 1 or −1 and neither of the variables can be eliminated by simply adding or subtracting the equations

Remember What You Learned

7. Think of an example of a system of linear equations you have seen earlier in this lesson. Explain what the benefits or drawbacks might be for using each of the methods for solving systems of linear equations. **See students' work.**

Chapter 5   34   Glencoe Algebra 1

Study Guide and Intervention page (left)

5-5 Study Guide and Intervention *(continued)*

Applying Systems of Linear Equations

APPLY SYSTEMS OF LINEAR EQUATIONS When applying systems of linear equations to problem situations, it is important to analyze each solution in the context of the situation.

Example **BUSINESS** A T-shirt printing company sells T-shirt for $15 each. The company has a fixed cost for the machine used to print the T-shirts and an additional cost per T-shirt. Use the table to estimate the number of T-shirts the company must sell in order for the income equal to expenses.

T-shirt Printing Cost	
Printing machine	$3000.00
blank T-shirt	$5.00

Explore You know the initial income and the initial expense and the rates of change of each quantity with each T-shirt sold.

Plan Write an equation to represent the income and the expenses. Then solve to find how many T-shirts need to be sold for both values to be equal.

Solve Let x = the number of T-shirts sold and let y = the total amount.

	total amount	=	initial amount	+	rate of change times number of T-shirts sold
income	y	=	0	+	$15x$
expenses	y	=	3000	+	$5x$

You can use substitution to solve this system.

$y = 15x$ The first equation.

$15x = 3000 + 5x$ Substitute the value for y into the second equation.

$10x = 3000$ Subtract $10x$ from each side and simplify.

$x = 300$ Divide each side by 10 and simplify.

This means that if 300 T-shirts are sold, the income and expenses of the T-shirt company are equal.

Check Does this solution make sense in the context of the problem? After selling 100 T-shirts, the income would be about $100 \times \$15$ or $1500. The costs would be about $\$3000 + 100 \times \$5$ or $3500.

Exercises

Refer to the example above. If the costs of the T-shirt company change to the given values and the selling price remains the same, determine the number of T-shirts the company must sell in order for income to equal expenses.

1. printing machine: $5000.00;
   T-shirt: $10.00 each   **1000**

2. printing machine: $2100.00;
   T-shirt: $8.00 each   **300**

3. printing machine: $8800.00;
   T-shirt: $4.00 each   **800**

4. printing machine: $1200.00;
   T-shirt: $12.00 each   **400**

Skills Practice page (right)

5-5 Skills Practice

Applying Systems of Linear Equations

Determine the best method to solve each system of equations. Then solve the system.

1. $5x + 3y = 16$
   $3x - 5y = -4$
   elimination ($\times$); (2, 2)

2. $3x - 5y = 7$
   $2x + 5y = 13$
   elimination (+); (4, 1)

3. $y = 3x - 24$
   $5x - y = 8$
   substitution; (-8, -48)

4. $-11x - 10y = 17$
   $5x - 7y = 50$
   elimination ($\times$); (3, -5)

5. $4x + y = 24$
   $5x - y = 12$
   elimination (+); (4, 8)

6. $6x - y = -145$
   $x = 4 - 2y$
   substitution; (-22, 13)

7. **VEGETABLE STAND** A roadside vegetable stand sells pumpkins for $5 each and squashes for $3 each. One day they sold 6 more squash than pumpkins, and their sales totaled $98. Write and solve a system of equations to find how many pumpkins and squash they sold? $y = 6 + x$ and $5x + 3y = 98$; 10 pumpkins, 16 squashes

8. **INCOME** Ramiro earns $20 per hour during the week and $30 per hour for overtime on the weekends. One week Ramiro earned a total of $650. He worked 5 times as many hours during the week as he did on the weekend. Write and solve a system of equations to determine how many hours of overtime Ramiro worked on the weekend.
$20x + 30y = 650$ and $x = 5y$; 5 hours

9. **BASKETBALL** Anya makes 14 baskets during her game. Some of these baskets were worth 2-points and others were worth 3-points. In total, she scored 30 points. Write and solve a system of equations to find how 2-points baskets she made.
$x + y = 14$ and $2x + 3y = 30$; 12

Answers

Page 39 — Word Problem Practice

NAME _____ DATE _____ PERIOD _____

5-5 Word Problem Practice

Applying Systems of Linear Equations

1. **MONEY** Veronica has been saving dimes and quarters. She has 94 coins in all, and the total value is $19.30. How many dimes and how many quarters does she have? **28 dimes; 66 quarters**

2. **CHEMISTRY** How many liters of 15% acid and 33% acid should be mixed to make 40 liters of 21% acid solution?

Concentration of Solution	Amount of Solution (L)	Amount of Acid
15%	x	
33%	y	
21%	40	

$26\frac{2}{3}$ L of 15%; $13\frac{1}{3}$ L of 33%

3. **BUILDINGS** The Sears Tower in Chicago is the tallest building in North America. The total height of the tower t and the antenna that stands on top of it a is 1729 feet. The difference in heights between the building and the antenna is 1171 feet. How tall is the Sears Tower? **1450 ft**

4. **PRODUCE** Roger and Trevor went shopping for produce on the same day. They each bought some apples and some potatoes. The amount they bought and the total price they paid are listed in the table below.

	Apples (lb)	Potatoes (lb)	Total Cost ($)
Roger	8	7	18.85
Trevor	2	10	12.88

What was the price of apples and potatoes per pound? **Apples: $1.49 per lb; Potatoes: $0.99 per lb**

5. **SHOPPING** Two stores are having a sale on T-shirts that normally sell for $20. Store S is advertising an s percent discount, and Store T is advertising a t dollar discount. Rose spends $63 for three T-shirts from Store S and one from Store T. Manny spends $140 on five T-shirts from Store S and four from Store T. Find the discount at each store. **Store S: 20%; Store T: $5**

TRANSPORTATION For Exercises 6–8 use the following information.

A Speedy River barge bound for New Orleans leaves Baton Rouge, Louisiana, at 9:00 A.M. and travels at a speed of 10 miles per hour. A Rail Transport freight train also bound for New Orleans leaves Baton Rouge at 1:30 P.M. the same day. The train travels at 25 miles per hour, and the river barge travels at 10 miles per hour. Both the barge and the train will travel 100 miles to reach New Orleans.

6. How far will the train travel before catching up to the barge? **75 mi**

7. Which shipment will reach New Orleans first? At what time? **The train will arrive first. It will arrive in New Orleans at 5:30 P.M. of the same day.**

8. If both shipments take an hour to unload before heading back to Baton Rouge, what is the earliest time that either one of the companies can begin to load grain to ship in Baton Rouge? **at 10:30 P.M. the same day**

Page 38 — Practice

NAME _____ DATE _____ PERIOD _____

5-5 Practice

Applying systems of Linear Equations

Determine the best method to solve each system of equations. Then solve the system.

1. $1.5x - 1.9y = -29$
   $x - 0.9y = 4.5$
   substitution; (63, 65)

2. $1.2x - 0.8y = -6$
   $4.8x + 2.4y = 60$
   elimination (×); (5, 15)

3. $18x - 16y = -312$
   $78x - 16y = 408$
   elimination (−); (12, 33)

4. $14x + 7y = 217$
   $14x + 3y = 189$
   elimination (−); (12, 7)

5. $x = 3.6y + 0.7$
   $2x + 0.2y = 38.4$
   substitution; (18.7, 5)

6. $5.3x - 4y = 43.5$
   $x + 7y = 78$
   substitution; (15, 9)

7. **BOOKS** A library contains 2000 books. There are 3 times as many non-fiction books as fiction books. Write and solve a system of equations to determine the number of non-fiction and fiction books. $x + y = 2000$ and $x = 3y$; **1500 non-fiction, 500 fiction**

8. **SCHOOL CLUBS** The chess club has 16 members and gains a new member every month. The film club has 4 members and gains 4 new members every month. Write and solve a system of equations to find when the number of members in both clubs will be equal. $y = 16 + x$ and $y = 4 + 4x$; **4x; 4 months**

For Exercises 9 and 10, use the information below.

Tia and Ken each sold snack bars and magazine subscriptions for a school fund-raiser, as shown in the table. Tia earned $132 and Ken earned $190.

	Number Sold	
Item	Tia	Ken
snack bars	16	20
magazine subscriptions	4	6

9. Define variable and formulate a system of linear equation from this situation. **Let x = the cost per snack bar and let y = the cost per magazine subscriptions; $16x + 4y = 132$ and $20x + 6y = 190$.**

10. What was the price per snack bar? Determine the reasonableness of your solution. **$2**

5-5 Enrichment

Cramer's Rule

Cramer's Rule is a method for solving a system of equations. To use Cramer's Rule, set up a matrix to represent the equations. A matrix is a way of organizing data.

Example Solve the following system of equations using Cramer's Rule.

$$2x + 3y = 13$$
$$x + y = 5$$

Step 1: Set up a matrix representing the coefficients of x and y.

$$A = \begin{vmatrix} x & y \\ 2 & 3 \\ 1 & 1 \end{vmatrix}$$

Step 2: Find the determinant of matrix A.

If a matrix $A = \begin{vmatrix} a & b \\ c & d \end{vmatrix}$, then the determinant, $\det(A) = ad - bc$.

$\det(A) = 2(1) - 1(3) = -1$

Step 3: Replace the first column in A with 13 and 5 and find the determinant of the new matrix.

$A_1 = \begin{vmatrix} 13 & 3 \\ 5 & 1 \end{vmatrix}$; $\det(A_1) = 13(1) - 5(3) = -2$

Step 4: To find the value of x in the solution to the system of equations, determine the value of $\frac{\det(A_1)}{\det(A)}$.

$\frac{\det(A_1)}{\det(A)} = \frac{-2}{-1}$ or 2

Step 5: Repeat the process to find the value of y. This time, replace the second column with 13 and 5 and find the determinant.

$A_2 = \begin{vmatrix} 2 & 13 \\ 1 & 5 \end{vmatrix}$; $\det(A_2) = 2(5) - 1(13) = -3$ and $\frac{\det(A_2)}{\det(A)} = \frac{-3}{-1}$ or 3.

So, the solution to the system of equations is (2, 3).

Exercises Use Cramer's Rule to solve each system of equations.

1. $2x + y = 1$
$3x + 5y = 5$
(0, 1)

2. $x + y = 4$
$2x - 3y = -2$
(2, 2)

3. $x - y = 4$
$3x - 5y = 8$
(6, 2)

4. $4x - y = 3$
$x + y = 7$
(2, 5)

5. $3x - 2y = 7$
$2x + y = 14$
(5, 4)

6. $6x - 5y = 1$
$3x + 2y = 5$
(1, 1)

Answers

Chapter 5 Assessment Answer Key

Quiz 1 (Lessons 5-1 and 5-2)
Page 43

1.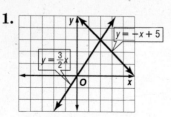

one solution; (2, 3)

2.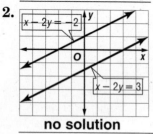

no solution

3. _____ (1, 5) _____

4. infinitely many solutions

5. _____ 23 weeks _____

Quiz 2 (Lesson 5-3)
Page 43

1. _____ $\left(5\frac{1}{2}, -1\frac{1}{2}\right)$

2. _____ $\left(-1\frac{1}{2}, 2\right)$

3. _____ $\left(2\frac{2}{3}, -1\frac{2}{9}\right)$

4. _____ $(-4, 2)$ _____

5. _____ -5 _____

Quiz 3 (Lesson 5-4)
Page 44

1. _____ $(-9, -5)$ _____

2. _____ $\left(3\frac{3}{5}, \frac{3}{5}\right)$

3. _____ $(-1, -1)$ _____

4. _____ $(2, -1)$ _____

5. _____ D _____

Quiz 4 (Lesson 5-5)
Page 44

1. substitution; (5, 2)

2. elimination using multiplication; (2, 3)

3. elimination using addition; (2.5, 1)

4. elimination using subtraction; (−2, −4)

5. _____ 4 videos _____

Mid-Chapter Test
Page 45

1. __ B __

2. __ C __

3. __ F __

4. __ C __

5. __ G __

6. __ D __

7.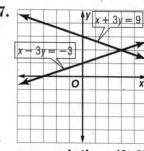

one solution; (3, 2)

8. _____ $(1, -4)$ _____

9. _____ $(16, -1)$ _____

10. _____ $(3, -2)$ _____

11. _____ $(-1, -4)$ _____

12. _____ 32 games _____

Chapter 5 Assessment Answer Key

Vocabulary Test
Page 46

1. system of equations

2. consistent

3. inconsistent

4. dependent

5. elimination

6. Sample answer: Substitution is a method of solving a system of equations where one variable is solved in terms of the other variable.

7. Sample answer: A system of equations that has exactly one solution is called independent.

Form 1
Page 47

1. C

2. F

3. G

4. H

5. A

6. G

7. C

8. G

9. B

10. H

11. D

Page 48

12. F

13. B

14. A

15. D

16. J

17. A

18. G

19. C

20. J

B: substitution; (0, 0)

Answers

Chapter 5 Assessment Answer Key

Form 2A
Page 49

1. A
2. B
3. J
4. A
5. F
6. C
7. H
8. A
9. H
10. B
11. J

Page 50

12. B
13. H
14. A
15. F
16. C
17. J
18. D
19. G
20. D

B: $\left(-7, -3\frac{1}{2}\right)$

Form 2B
Page 51

1. C
2. B
3. H
4. B
5. J
6. A
7. H
8. D
9. F
10. C
11. H

Page 52

12. B
13. G
14. C
15. J
16. A
17. F
18. B
19. J
20. C

B: Manuel is 15 years old; his sister is 7 years old.

Chapter 5 Assessment Answer Key

1. **no solution**

2. **one solution**

3.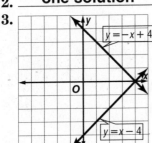

one solution; (4, 0)

4.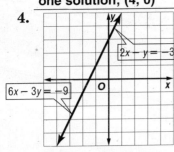

infinitely many solutions

5.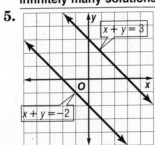

no solution

6. **(1, 3)**

7. **(3, 5)**

8. **no solution**

9. **infinitely many solutions**

10. **(−8, 0)**

11. **(4, −1)**

12. **(−3, 2)**

13. **(7, −1)**

14. **(2, 1)**

15. **(13, 1)**

16. **substitution; (3, 2)**

17. **elimination with subtraction; (2, −7)**

18. **elimination with multiplication; (0, 5)**

19. **elimination with addition; (2, −3)**

20. **23 and −6**

21. **186 student tickets; 135 adult tickets**

22. **14 dimes; 19 nickels**

23. **28 square miles**

24. **Sample answer:**
x = hours per standard fan;
y = hours per econoomy fan;
$3x + 3y = 1500$
$2x + y = 800$

25. **300 standard fans**

B: **Mavis is 15 years old; her brother is 10 years old.**

Answers

Chapter 5 Assessment Answer Key

Form 2D
Page 55

1. infinitely many solutions

2. one solution

3.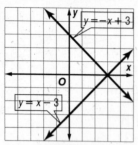

one solution; (3, 0)

4.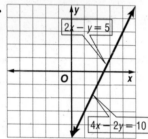

infinitely many solutions

5.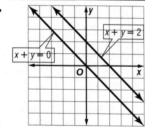

no solution

6. (2, 4)

7. (2, 1)

8. infinitely many solutions

9. no solution

10. (5, 3)

11. (2, 2)

12. (−1, 4)

13. (−2, 5)

14. (7, −3)

15. (6, −2)

Page 56

16. substitution; (−2, −5)

17. elimination with subtraction; (−1,1)

18. elimination with multiplication; (−1, 5)

19. elimination with addition; (3, 2)

20. 18 and −2

21. 34 hours

22. 5 two-point goals; 11 three-point goals

23. 129 square miles

24. Sample answer:
x = speakers on Tadashi 200;
y = speakers on Tadashi 500;
$2x + 3y = 900$
$2x + 4y = 1000$

25. 300 Tadashi 200 phone systems

B: (−1, −3)

Chapter 5 Assessment Answer Key

Form 3
Page 57

Page 58

1.

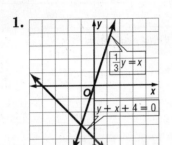

one solution; $(-1, -3)$

2.

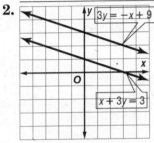

no solution

3.

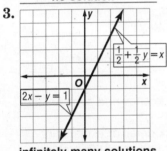

infinitely many solutions

4. $(4, 1)$

5. no solution

6. $(-22, -6)$

7. infinitely many solutions

8. $(1, 2)$

9. no solution

10. $\left(3, -\dfrac{3}{7}\right)$

11. $(-14, 7)$

12. $(-2, -6)$

13. $(-32, 15)$

14. $(6, 14)$

15. $(-2, 6)$

16. substitution; $(63, 84)$

17. elimination using multiplication; $\left(-\dfrac{1}{2}, \dfrac{1}{2}\right)$

18. elimination using addition; $(2, -4)$

19. elimination using subtraction; $(-19, 3)$

20. 6, 10

21. $3\dfrac{1}{2}, 8\dfrac{1}{2}$

22. 67

23. 10 lb of $2.45 mix; 20 lb of $2.30 mix

24. 5 mph

25. 1250 bushels of barley

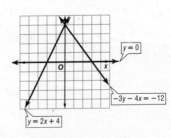

B: 10 square units

Chapter 5 Assessment Answer Key

Page 59, Extended-Response Test
Scoring Rubric

Score	General Description	Specific Criteria
4	**Superior** A correct solution that is supported by well-developed, accurate explanations	• Shows thorough understanding of the concepts of *solving systems of equations*. • Uses appropriate strategies to solve problems. • Computations are correct. • Written explanations are exemplary. • Graphs are accurate and appropriate. • Goes beyond requirements of some or all problems.
3	**Satisfactory** A generally correct solution, but may contain minor flaws in reasoning or computation	• Shows an understanding of the concepts of *solving systems of equations*. • Uses appropriate strategies to solve problems. • Computations are mostly correct. • Written explanations are effective. • Graphs are mostly accurate and appropriate. • Satisfies all requirements of problems.
2	**Nearly Satisfactory** A partially correct interpretation and/or solution to the problem	• Shows an understanding of most of the concepts of *solving systems of equations*. • May not use appropriate strategies to solve problems. • Computations are mostly correct. • Written explanations are satisfactory. • Graphs are mostly accurate. • Satisfies the requirements of most of the problems.
1	**Nearly Unsatisfactory** A correct solution with no supporting evidence or explanation	• Final computation is correct. • No written explanations or work is shown to substantiate the final computation. • Graphs may be accurate but lack detail or explanation. • Satisfies minimal requirements of some of the problems.
0	**Unsatisfactory** An incorrect solution indicating no mathematical understanding of the concept or task, or no solution is given	• Shows little or no understanding of most of the concepts of *solving systems of equations*. • Does not use appropriate strategies to solve problems. • Computations are incorrect. • Written explanations are unsatisfactory. • Graphs are inaccurate or inappropriate. • Does not satisfy requirements of problems. • No answer may be given.

Chapter 5 Assessment Answer Key

Page 59, Extended-Response Test
Sample Answers

In addition to the scoring rubric found on page A26, the following sample answers may be used as guidance in evaluating extended-response assessment items.

1a. Sample answer: (5000, 5000); $600

1b. (15,000, −5000); To represent a possible investment both x and y must be positive. Thus, there is no interpretation for a negative value for y.

2a. The student should recognize that the total cost of a one-day rental of a compact car from the car rental company is modeled by the equation $y = A + Bx$, where y is the total cost and x is the number of miles driven during the day. Likewise, the total cost of a one-day rental of a compact car from the leading competitor is modeled by the equation $y = 15 + 0.25x$. The solution to the system is the number of miles driven during the day that makes the cost of renting a compact car from the two companies for one day equal, and the corresponding total cost.

2b. The value of A determines if the one-day fee for the rental of the compact car from the car rental company will be less than, greater than, or equal to the one-day fee from their leading competitor. The value of B determines whether the number of miles driven will keep the total cost less than, greater than, or equal to the total cost of renting from the leading competitor, or change which company has the higher total cost for the rental.

3a. $x + y = S$
$2.5x + 0.75y = P$
Both S and P must be positive. The student may recognize that the maximum profit is 2.5 times the weekly sales, and the minimum profit is 0.75 times the weekly sales. i.e., $0.75S \le P \le 2.5S$.

3b. Sample answer:

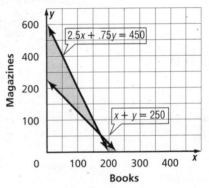

The graph of this system of equations shows the ordered pair that corresponds to weekly sales of 250 and a weekly profit of $450. In order to have a profit of $450 from magazine and book sales, the store would have to sell 150 books and 100 magazines.

Answers

Chapter 5 Assessment Answer Key

Standardized Test Practice

Page 60

1. ● Ⓑ Ⓒ Ⓓ

2. ● Ⓖ Ⓗ Ⓙ

3. Ⓐ Ⓑ ● Ⓓ

4. Ⓕ Ⓖ ● Ⓙ

5. Ⓐ Ⓑ Ⓒ ●

6. ● Ⓖ Ⓗ Ⓙ

7. Ⓐ ● Ⓒ Ⓓ

8. Ⓕ ● Ⓗ Ⓙ

9. Ⓐ ● Ⓒ Ⓓ

10. Ⓕ ● Ⓗ Ⓙ

Page 61

11. Ⓐ Ⓑ Ⓒ ●

12. ● Ⓖ Ⓗ Ⓙ

13. Ⓐ ● Ⓒ Ⓓ

14. Ⓕ Ⓖ ● Ⓙ

15. Ⓐ ● Ⓒ Ⓓ

16. ● Ⓖ Ⓗ Ⓙ

17. Ⓐ Ⓑ Ⓒ ●

18.

			1	.			
⓪	⓪	⓪	⓪		⓪	⓪	⓪
①	①	①	●		①	①	①
②	②	②	②		②	②	②
③	③	③	③		③	③	③
④	④	④	④		④	④	④
⑤	⑤	⑤	⑤		⑤	⑤	⑤
⑥	⑥	⑥	⑥		⑥	⑥	⑥
⑦	⑦	⑦	⑦		⑦	⑦	⑦
⑧	⑧	⑧	⑧		⑧	⑧	⑧
⑨	⑨	⑨	⑨		⑨	⑨	⑨

19.

			8	.			
⓪	⓪	⓪	⓪		⓪	⓪	⓪
①	①	①	①		①	①	①
②	②	②	②		②	②	②
③	③	③	③		③	③	③
④	④	④	④		④	④	④
⑤	⑤	⑤	⑤		⑤	⑤	⑤
⑥	⑥	⑥	⑥		⑥	⑥	⑥
⑦	⑦	⑦	⑦		⑦	⑦	⑦
⑧	⑧	⑧	●		⑧	⑧	⑧
⑨	⑨	⑨	⑨		⑨	⑨	⑨

Chapter 5 Assessment Answer Key

Standardized Test Practice
Page 62

20. _____102_____

21. _____21_____

22. _____$\{(-4, -2), (-2, -1.5),$ $(0, -1), (2, -0.5), (4, 0)\}$_____

23. _____$y = 4x - 4$_____

24. _____$a \leq -15$_____

25. _____$x = 10$_____

26. _____no solution_____

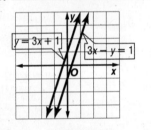

27. _____7, 14_____

28. _____$(7, -3)$_____

29.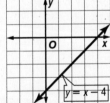

30a. _____Sample answer:
$25 + 55h = C$
$40 + 30h = C$_____

30b. _____$\dfrac{3}{5}$ hour_____